MW00414079

RETREAT

SANCTUARY AND SELF-CARE FOR EVERY DAY

SALLY BROCKWAY

vie

RETREAT

An Hachette UK Company
www.hachette.co.uk

Vie Books, an imprint of Summersdale Publishers Ltd
Part of Octopus Publishing Group Limited
Carmelite House
50 Victoria Embankment
LONDON
EC4Y 0DZ
UK

Printed and bound in China

ISBN: 978-1-78783-644-0

DISCLAIMER

Where remedies are offered in this book, please conduct your own supplementary research and consult a trained professional to determine what is appropriate for you. When using essential oils, remember that these natural substances can have powerful effects, so it's wise to test a small amount on your skin to check for any reaction. Always consult a physician before use, particularly if you are pregnant, nursing or have a known health complaint.

Neither the author nor the publisher can be held responsible for any loss or claim arising out of the use, or misuse, of the suggestions made herein.

CONTENTS

Part Three: Retreat Away 103

INTRODUCTION

Take a deep breath and relax. It's time to retreat to a time and space where you get to switch off and chill, do stuff you love, eat food that makes you feel fantastic, sleep, read, stretch and take long, hot baths - or anything else that helps you unwind. There are a thousand ways to retreat from a busy life and grab some life-affirming me time, and this book aims to inspire and help you discover what works for you.

Not taking time out is a bit like riding a bicycle without ever pumping up the tyres or oiling the chain – eventually, it's going to stop working so well.

The benefits of going on retreat are enormous. Stepping back from day-to-day life can ease anxiety, spark creativity and aid sleep. It also gives you a chance to reflect on your life. If you don't do that occasionally, you may race down the wrong path and end up in a job, relationship or friendship group that's not quite right for you. A busy life can be an awesome one, but to be your best, happiest and healthiest self, you have to experience life in the slow lane, too.

Don't worry, there's no requirement to book off entire weekends to go on retreat (although it's great if you can do exactly that sometimes). You can experience the benefits regularly by putting aside just five minutes now and then – and, while there are lots of wonderful organized retreats all over the world offering anything from crafting through to yoga and writing, spending money is not a prerequisite. Retreat is a state of mind and you can experience it anywhere: at home, abroad, in the shower, your back garden, a castle, a farm or deep in the woods. The choice is yours.

PART ONE

RETREAT AT HOME

To enjoy the retreat experience on a regular basis without breaking the bank, look for ways to create a sanctuary in your own home. It doesn't matter if you flat-share, live with a partner or have noisy kids, because it's almost always possible to find a small slice of quiet space – you might just have to get creative.

It's worth learning to use your home as a tool to relax and unwind, as it will mean that you can enjoy retreat vibes at any time, whenever they're needed. It might take a bit of planning to create a staying-in retreat experience, but it will pay off. If you do share your living space with others, explain why it is important for you to enjoy some quiet time and, if you have to, buy yourself a "Do not disturb" sign that you can hang on a doorknob.

GET A DOWNTIME HABIT

Retreat time should be as much a part of your schedule as regular exercise, social outings and going to the supermarket. It's important, which means you need to make time for it. If you really believe that you don't have any spare moments to retreat, then you need to do it more than most!

It's easier to find time than you might think. How many hours do you spend streaming TV shows and movies? How much of your precious time does social media fritter away? Can you get up an hour earlier?

There is probably space in your diary for retreat and you only need to step away from your busyness for five minutes to notice an improvement in your overall well-being.

The best way to start is to commit to a time for some retreat space. Block it out in your diary, as that will help you turn it into a habit. Attempt to take at least one chunk of retreat time each week, although you can always have more if you like.

Don't beat yourself up if you miss your slot. Try to reschedule it immediately and don't let too much time slip by, because then your retreat habit will become less of a priority in your mind.

Set up alerts on your devices or use a particular highlighter colour to mark your retreat time, if you use a paper diary, and write yourself reminders on sticky notes – when you look at them, you'll remember that you have a lovely appointment in your calendar to look forward to.

TURN YOUR HOME INTO A SANCTUARY

When preparing your home for retreat, imagine that someone you admire or look up to is coming over. This sends a strong message to the part of your brain that is outside your conscious awareness, where all your beliefs, impulses and patterns of behaviour are stored. You're declaring that you're not prepared to chill out among piles of dirty laundry and half-eaten pizza, because you value yourself. This time is sacred and you deserve the very best.

It's recommended that you declutter and do a deep clean before you commit to regular retreat time at home. This creates a space that is soothing, somewhere you can relax quietly and lose yourself in whatever it is you are doing.

If you've been meaning to Marie Kondo your closet for ages or have piles of things scattered about that you've been planning to sort, then now is the time to do it. A clean, clear space will really help to quieten your mind when it comes to your precious time out.

You might like to hang uplifting pictures, scatter a few healthy houseplants around the place and decorate it with ornaments, crystals or good-luck charms. Look through your favourite magazines for interior inspiration.

Think about all your senses, not just what you can see. Is the space comfortable? Can you get some peace and quiet? And does it smell nice?

You could also compile a mood board to hang in your retreat space. This is a large piece of card filled with images and words that sum up exactly how you want to feel when you are on retreat. It will ensure that those emotions are never far from your mind, even when you're not taking time out.

CAMPFIRE

ESSENTIAL OILS

To help create an atmosphere of blissful calm in your home, try an essential-oil spritz. All it takes is a few sprays around a room for it to be suffused with a glorious, soothing fragrance.

Ingredients

Distilled water
80–100 drops of essential oil of your choice*
A spray bottle or plant mister

Method

- Add the water and oil to the spray bottle or plant mister, shake the contents well and then spray. A few squirts will leave a glorious aroma that will linger in the air.

** There are lots of essential oils available, each with its own properties. Find one that suits you, with a scent you love. For a calming environment, you can choose between lavender, camomile, bergamot, frankincense, and rose. And, of course, you can experiment and combine your favourite fragrances or purchase a ready-mixed blend designed to encourage inner calm and restfulness.*

Here are ten essential oils that are great for the home. You can add a few drops to your cleaning products, or use them in diffusers or a spritz bottle to fill your surroundings with wonderful smells:

- **Lemon** – smells clean, fresh and invigorating.
- **Rosemary** – makes your home smell like a spa.
- **Wild orange** – a fresh, warm scent that works well in the kitchen.
- **Eucalyptus** – ideal if you are suffering from congestion; a nice option for the bathroom.
- **Peppermint** – a refreshing minty aroma that is ideal for the bathroom.
- **Pine** – a lovely woody fragrance that creates the atmosphere of a lush green forest.
- **Thyme** – invigorating; perfect if you want clarity of thought.
- **Cinnamon** – neutralizes cooking smells.
- **Rose** – soothing in the bedroom.
- **Geranium** – an uplifting floral fragrance.

MAKE YOUR OWN BALMS AND LOTIONS

Although you can buy any number of oils, lotions and bath concoctions to help you get that spa experience at home, it is easy to make your own, and this can become a special part of the whole retreat experience.

Here are two lovely things you can create yourself to inject bliss and gorgeousness into your home retreat.

MINT BALM

The fresh and cooling scent of mint is ideal for reducing tension. Once you've made it, this soothing balm can be stored in a small jar or tin for up to six months. You can carry it with you or keep it for use in the home. A few dabs massaged into the temples can help ease headaches.

Ingredients

200 ml sunflower oil
2 tbsp dried mint leaves, crushed
20–30 drops of peppermint oil
50 g beeswax

Method

- Place the oil and mint leaves in a heavy-based pan and simmer on a low heat for an hour.
- Remove from the heat, allow it to cool and strain, keeping the oil and discarding the mint leaves.
- Add the peppermint oil drops to the infused sunflower oil.
- Next, melt the beeswax in a bowl over a bain-marie and once it is liquid, stir in the infused oil.
- Pour all the liquid into a glass bottle or a jar with a screw top.

SANDALWOOD BALM

When used as a fragrance, sandalwood is thought to promote mental clarity and calm, and to balance your mood. Make your very own balm using this recipe and allow the woody scent to help you relax. Rub it on the wrists and ankles to ease a stressful day.

Ingredients

6 drops of sandalwood essential oil
2 drops of rose essential oil
4 tsp sweet almond oil

Method

- Mix the essential oils into the sweet almond oil and store in an airtight jar. You should always mix essential oils with another oil, known as a "carrier oil", such as sweet almond. This is because they are highly concentrated and should never be applied directly to the skin.

THE TEN-MINUTE RECHARGE

Just ten minutes away from your hectic life can help you to clear your head, and feel calmer and more relaxed – what you decide to do in that time is up to you (although it is recommended that you choose something calming and avoid frenetic activities)!

A good way to start is by simply stepping away, whether it be from the computer screen, your office, chores, dashing around or socializing. You don't have to tell anyone what you are doing – just take a break. Go outside or find somewhere quiet indoors to sit, without your mobile phone to hand. Doing absolutely nothing for ten minutes can really help to ease tension.

Take a few deep breaths, and imagine you are inhaling energy and exhaling any tightness. Notice what's going on inside. How do you feel? Are there any aches and pains in your body? There's no need to do anything – you're just taking note.

Sometimes the simple act of checking in with your emotions and your environment is enough to ease stress and help you to forget any worries that might be whirling around your mind.

A ten-minute walk, preferably outdoors, will do wonders for your mood during a busy day – and if you can go somewhere near nature, even better. If you are in the middle of a town, seek out trees or a nearby park. Pay attention to the setting and appreciate the beauty or stunning architecture around you, or simply look up at the sky.

It's easy to get carried away by the day's events, so set an alarm to remind yourself to take ten minutes out. You never know, you might start a new trend among your workmates and friends.

You can also use your ten minutes as a tea or snack break. Avoid sugary, fatty or overly processed foods for maximum benefits. Likewise, choosing a decaffeinated coffee or tea, or a herbal variety, is better for you. There's nothing wrong with a good strong coffee or tea, but caffeine is a stimulant and will make it harder for you to wind down.

If there is no way of getting out and you really need a break, find a window with a decent view, open it a crack (depending on the weather) and look out. Allow yourself the luxury of gazing at the scene for ten minutes, noticing all the details out there – the movements, the sounds, the clouds, and so on. If you're wrestling with a problem, sometimes a few moments staring out of the window can encourage the solution to appear.

YOUR OWN BATHROOM SPA

With a few finishing touches, you can create a bespoke spa experience in your own bathroom to soothe away the stresses and strains of everyday life.

Start by ensuring the place is as clean as you can make it and get rid of any clutter. Be merciless with your bathroom – throw out any mouldy shower caps, rusty razors and ancient bath soaks. Of course, if you don't want to throw things out, you can always hide them in a cupboard.

Now is the perfect time to invest in some quality towels. Most of us keep going with the same ones we've had for years, not noticing that they are rough on the skin. You could invest in some luxury towels and reserve them for spa days – that way, you'll feel as if you're getting a real five-star experience.

The same goes for your bath mat: if it is threadbare and old, swap it for something soft and fluffy that will feel nice on your toes. And why not treat yourself to a fluffy towelling bathrobe to save for spa days?

Think about your bathroom storage. Is it as stylish as it could be? Sometimes all it takes is a lick of paint on a piece of furniture you found in a second-hand sale to create a pretty bathroom cabinet perfect for displaying all your bottles and tubes.

For a wonderful aroma, sprinkle essential oils around the base of your shower before you get in. When the hot water hits them, a heavenly steam will be released and your bathroom will smell like a fancy spa hotel. Remember to run the water for a few seconds before entering the shower, so that your skin doesn't make contact with the concentrated oil.

Lighting scented candles creates a lovely atmosphere in your bathroom. Also, if you have the space, consider bringing in a Bluetooth speaker so that you can listen to relaxing music while you soak.

LUXURIOUS HANDMADE SPA PRODUCTS

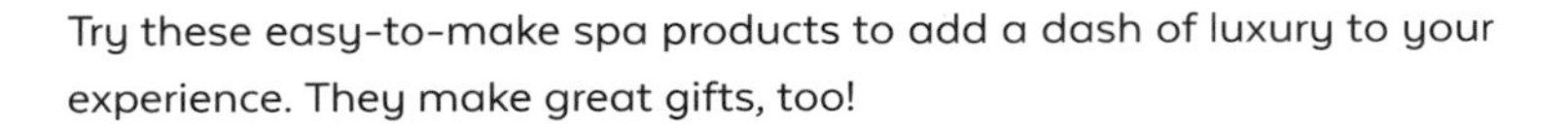

Try these easy-to-make spa products to add a dash of luxury to your experience. They make great gifts, too!

JOYFUL BATH BOMB

Ingredients

100 g baking soda
50 g Epsom salts
25 g rose petals
1 tsp rose oil
1 tsp rose-hip oil
Red food colouring (optional)
50 g citric acid

Method

- Place the dry ingredients in a bowl and mix well.
- Mix the wet ingredients in a separate jug.
- Gradually pour the wet mix into the dry, stirring constantly.
- When they are combined, pack into a mould of your choice – two identical small bowls work well to create a ball.
- Allow the bomb to dry before adding it to a warm bath.

STRESS-BUSTING FOOTBATH

There's nothing like plunging your tired feet into a soothing footbath – and adding some calming herbs really enhances the experience. You could make this a daily bedtime ritual.

Ingredients

Any mix of the following dried herbs:
Camomile
Lemon balm
Lavender
Rose petals

Method

- Place 100 g of the herb mix in 2 litres of warm water in a pan.
- Bring to the boil and simmer for 30 minutes.
- Remove from the heat, leave for an hour and strain.
- Reheat the water before use and add to a basin big enough to wiggle your feet in – the average washing-up bowl will take around 4 litres of water and 200 g of herbs.
- Plunge your feet in and soak for as long as you like!

UNPLUG

It's a really good idea to unplug all your electronic devices and leave them switched off during your retreat experience – otherwise, they'll be pinging away and you might be tempted to check your messages. When you step away from your normal busy schedule, your mind slows down, but if you keep looking at a screen, it'll speed right up again.

Did you know that the light that comes off your mobile phone or tablet stimulates the production of hormones that make you feel alert? This can make it difficult for you to relax and it can also interrupt your sleep patterns, which is why it's wise to avoid too much screen time just before bed. There are useful apps and settings on most phones which will filter out the offending blue light, as well as reducing the intensity and brilliance of the screen display, which may help you sleep better. They have names like "night light" or "blue light filter".

If you feel jittery with your phone switched off, it might be worth taking a closer look at your relationship with the device. A study from the UK Post Office discovered that some people find going without their phones as scary as a trip to the dentist and it named the condition "nomophobia".

Studies have also shown that staring at screens for too long can cause eye strain, characterized by blurred vision and dry eyes. It's something that most of us have experienced and it does us good to take a break once in a while. There is also some evidence that spending too much time on smart devices can cause headaches, plus craning to look at a screen for too long can impact on the nerves in the spine and neck – the term "text neck" has been coined to describe the pains that this can cause. There have also been incidences of people experiencing elbow and thumb strain from phone use.

There is no need to ditch the smartphone, but if you can break your addiction (if you have one) or take regular breaks without it, you'll feel a lot better!

If you are used to jotting ideas down on your mobile phone, keep a notebook by your side during your retreat so that anything that springs to mind doesn't get forgotten.

GO SLOW

Whatever you choose to do during your retreat time – whether it be baking, bathing or going for a walk – doing it at a slow pace is a must. You are taking a break from your hectic schedule, so you don't want to add any more "tasks" that feel like hard work.

Savour every moment of your retreat time: there is no rush, no prize for getting to the end. It is essential that you slow down if you want to relax. For some, this is difficult, so be gentle with yourself and remember that it will get better with practice.

Put your to-do list to one side and practise slowing the pace for 15 minutes. For example, you could have a candlelit bath without distractions. Staying there for 15 minutes will allow you to luxuriate in the water and appreciate any lovely smells or soothing background music. If you're a person who's always on the go, you might find that you feel uncomfortable during your relaxation time. This could be because you are addicted to busyness, perhaps even using it as a distraction to avoid any awkward emotions that lurk beneath the surface. It's perfectly natural to feel like this, but try to stay with it, as it gets easier over time and the unease will pass. Take some deep breaths and try to be as "in the moment" as you can. This means not getting tangled up in your thoughts, but instead noticing what's going on around you.

Life is short – don't let it pass you by in a flash; slow down and enjoy the journey.

SLOWING-DOWN EXPERIMENT

Pick a short walking route in your local area that you take regularly, then walk the route as if this were the last time you will ever do it. Take a look around; what do you see?

When you are fully engaged with your surroundings, you'll notice that you are more than likely walking at a far slower pace than normal. You will probably surprise yourself by spotting things you've walked past a thousand times but never noticed before.

Remember this experience when you next walk that particular route.

A BLISSFUL BEDROOM

Aside from the bathroom, one of the best places in the home to enjoy retreat time is the bedroom, since it is associated with relaxation and includes a bed that you can sink into!

If your bedroom does not feel restful, give it a quick makeover. Have a browse online and look at how commercial retreat centres decorate. Choose colours, fabrics and artwork that soothe. Lighting makes a big difference, too – rather than stark overhead lights, use lamps and candles (make sure they don't pose a fire risk, though).

One item worth spending money on is good-quality sheets, as they will give you that luxury hotel feeling every time you climb into bed. For a real pampering touch, choose a higher thread count: between 400 and 800. Hopefully, you have a decent mattress, too!

Make your bed before retreating to your room. If it looks orderly, it will help to calm your mind. If you haven't already got them, invest in some lovely blankets or a throw to keep yourself cosy. It's also good to have a shawl, something made from a soft material that will feel wonderful against your skin.

A chair is desirable, too, but it needs to be a comfortable one! You might like to meditate there, gaze out of the window or write in your journal. It will give your back a break if you've spent a long time lounging on the bed. A yoga mat is also a useful addition, as it's good to stretch regularly during retreat time.

Freshen the air with an essential-oil spritz, potpourri, a reed diffuser, a room spray or an essential-oils vaporizer. Relaxing scents like lavender, rose, bergamot, camomile, ylang-ylang and rosemary work well in the bedroom. Before using any essential oils, it's recommended that you open the window to allow some fresh air in. If you have allergies, consider using an air purifier.

If you have space and it's convenient, put a kettle in your bedroom – you might be tempted to do the washing-up if you keep going into the kitchen. You could have to hand a selection of herbal teas in a jar or some sprigs of herbs, so that you can make fresh brews like this lemon balm infusion.

LEMON BALM INFUSION

Ingredients

2 sprigs of fresh
lemon balm
250 ml boiled water

Method

- Place the lemon balm in a cup and pour boiling water over the leaves.
- By the time the liquid is cool enough to drink, the lemon balm leaves will have infused their delicate and refreshing flavour.

HOME-MADE ROOM FRAGRANCES

It is imperative that your chosen room smells heavenly when you take time out to retreat! There are plenty of products on the market for freshening up the home, but you can make your own, too. Try these simple odour-busting recipes.

CARPET FRESHENER

Ingredients

230 g baking soda
1 tbsp ground cinnamon

Method

- Mix the two ingredients and add them to a shaker container – if you don't have one, simply use your hands.
- Sprinkle the powder liberally on the carpet and allow it to stand for an hour, before vacuuming as usual. Your carpet will smell fantastic!

SIMMERING SCENT

By filling a saucepan with aromatic ingredients, you can create a scent that will fill your home.

Ingredients

1 sliced orange
1 sliced lemon
2 cinnamon sticks
4 whole cloves
1 bay leaf
1 tbsp honey

Method

- Add the ingredients to a saucepan.
- Half-fill with water.
- Place a lid on the pan, but leave a crack for steam to escape.
- Simmer for a couple of hours.
- Check the water levels and don't allow the pan to dry out.
- You could put a pan on in advance and turn the hob off if you don't want to keep nipping into the kitchen during your relaxation time.

Tips for great-smelling clothes

To make your clothes smell wonderful, try adding 10–20 drops of your favourite essential oil to your wash. You can also hang small fabric bags of dried lavender in your closet or spray some tissue paper with your favourite perfume and tuck them between your clothes. If you have moths in the house, pieces of cedar wood will both repel them and scent your garments nicely.

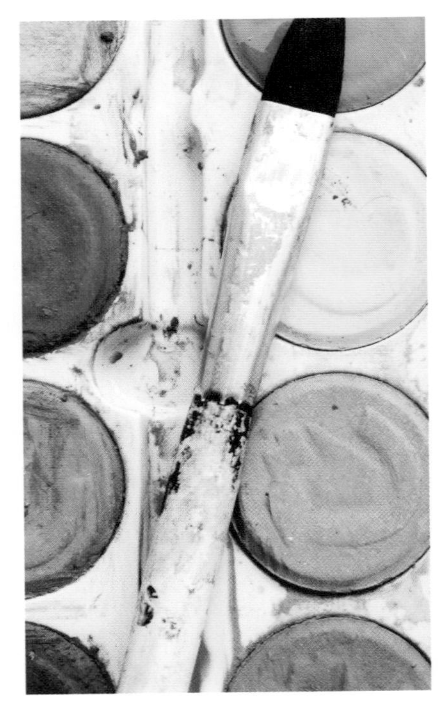

RETREAT ACTIVITIES

Being on retreat doesn't mean you have to lie around and meditate the whole time – anything that relaxes you and encourages the mind to slow down will be beneficial. We're all different and while some like to spend hours writing, others prefer baking or tinkering with car engines. Find what works for you!

The activity that allows you to switch off best is often what you do for the sheer joy of it. Perhaps you have a dog and love going for long walks or you spend your spare time fishing. This doesn't mean you shouldn't try anything new, though, as retreat time is ideal for tapping into hidden aspects of yourself or trying things you've always fancied doing.

Wherever possible, choose an activity that absorbs you to a point where you are no longer aware of time passing, so that you'll look up and wonder where all the hours went. It is often the simplest of tasks that achieve this for us, such as colouring in or reading.

Any activity that absorbs you is a form of meditation, as it gently encourages you to focus on what you are doing rather than worry about the past or future. Research shows that this can ease anxiety and depression, and help you to sleep better.

Don't do anything that you really don't enjoy – getting to grips with your admin or tidying up your wardrobes, for example, won't necessarily rejuvenate you unless you get a kick out of organizing!

Whatever you choose, do it mindfully. This involves paying full attention to the task. Feel the joy of it and engage all your senses. Avoid multitasking, by limiting yourself to one activity, as this will enable you to concentrate better. Again, it is best to avoid the TV and radio – and to switch off mobile devices – so that you don't get side-tracked by social media or messages.

SELF-LOVE

To get the most out of your retreat time it helps if you learn to love yourself. Self-love is about more than feeling good; it's about being your own biggest fan.

TIPS TO CULTIVATE SELF-LOVE

Get to know yourself. Sit quietly and ask: "How do I feel?" What's going on with your emotions? Relax and invite them in. If negative emotions surface, don't panic – they will pass through and be released, if you don't resist them.

Self-care. Look after yourself. It is possible to put yourself first without being selfish. If you don't meet your own needs, how can you be expected to look after anyone else's? Make an effort to eat well, and consume a rainbow mix of fruits and vegetables. Allow yourself treats too and never ban certain foods, as this will only leave you wanting them more. Finally, make sure you get at least 20 minutes of exercise per day. You don't have to break out into a sweat – a brisk walk will do.

Set clear boundaries. *Don't allow yourself to be coerced into doing things you'd rather not, whether it be a family holiday or a night out with friends. Be honest with others and don't worry too much what other people think.*

Be kind to yourself. *Treat yourself the way you would treat a small child or a friend: you wouldn't punish them or try to make them feel guilty if they got something wrong. You're doing a great job. Take time to look at how far you've come.*

Accept that you are in charge of your own destiny. *Actively choose the kind of life you want to live and follow your dreams. Yes, there will be setbacks and things might not always go your way, but with the right mindset you can achieve anything.*

Reward yourself. *Set up a new bank or savings account and label it "fun" or "treats", or anything that inspires and excites you. This is for money to be spent on things that make you feel good. Designer jeans, restaurant meals, holidays – whatever it is that makes you happy. Commit to putting a percentage of your income into the account every time you get paid. It shouldn't take long before you have enough cash to spoil yourself.*

Avoid toxic relationships. *You don't need to take on anybody else's problems or put up with toxic behaviour. Treat yourself like a god or goddess who only deserves the best and won't accept anything less. Don't be unkind, but be firm and make sure you spend the majority of your time with those who love you and make you feel good about life.*

MEDITATION

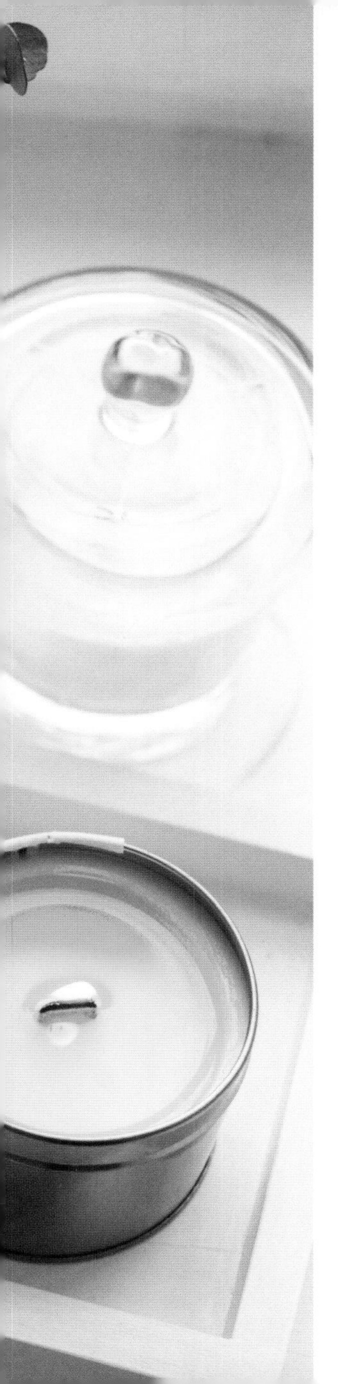

Meditation is the practice of calming a busy mind and gently teaching it how to stay centred in among the chaos of everyday life. People who meditate regularly are less stressed, have better concentration and enjoy higher energy levels. Studies show that meditating for ten minutes increases the brain's alpha waves – this is associated with relaxation and a decrease in anxiety and depression.

You can meditate anywhere, at any time – all you need is peace and quiet. Ensure that you won't be disturbed, as you will be focusing on yourself during your entire meditation.

There is no pass or fail with meditating. It will be different every session. Rather than aspire to an outcome, observe what happens with interest and keep a meditation diary – doing this will enable you to chart your progress and notice any patterns.

TEN-MINUTE MEDITATION

- Sit comfortably with your back straight and eyes closed.
- Take a deep breath in and exhale slowly. Feel the sensation of the air travelling in and out of your lungs. Do this three times.
- Do a mental scan of your body, starting with your toes and moving up to the top of your head.
- Imagine the tension releasing from each area of your body in turn.
- Count your breaths from one to ten and repeat. If you find your mind wandering, bring it back to your breathing. If you find it easier, you can repeat one word or a short mantra in your head to focus the mind.

MINDFULNESS

Mindfulness is a state you enter when your mind is fully engaged in whatever it is doing in the present moment. You're not thinking about the past or the future – you are totally engrossed in what's happening right now.

Everybody is born with the ability to be mindful. Young children slip into the state with ease, but as we grow older, the stresses and strains of everyday life can take over and then we have to relearn how to access this part of ourselves.

You can be mindful at any time of day. If you are new to the practice, try it for five minutes at least once a day. It has a cumulative effect, so don't expect results right away. Make it a habit and you are likely to start feeling more relaxed and in control of your emotions.

There are various mindfulness apps available which offer short sessions and you could also try classes or books. There is a lot of information out there on mindfulness and, as with everything, the trick is to find the methods that suit *you*.

SIMPLE MINDFULNESS EXERCISE

- Choose an object that is close by and focus on it. This will work best if you choose something that is naturally pleasing to the eye, such as a flower or your favourite ornament.
- Relax and keep looking at it.
- Imagine you are seeing this object for the first time and explore it with your eyes.
- If you get caught up with thoughts, gently bring yourself back to looking at the object.
- Breathe slowly and deeply, and try to relax.
- Allow yourself to be captivated by the object for as long as you can.

EVERYDAY MINDFULNESS

Try this mindfulness exercise when you are doing mundane chores or something repetitive – this is a good one to attempt while you are doing the washing-up or cleaning.

- Focus 100 per cent on your task.
- Be aware of the sensations in your body as you work.
- Listen to the sounds you make and any other noises in the background.
- If your mind drifts, bring it back to the task.

SLEEP IS THE BEST MEDICINE

Sleep is one of the most important aspects of our daily lives, as the body is hard at work restoring, repairing and strengthening while we dream.

It is recommended that adults have between seven and nine hours of sleep each night. Yet, according to the Centers for Disease Control and Prevention, 35 per cent of adults don't get enough sleep and this puts them at risk of increased anxiety levels, memory issues, diabetes, poor balance and high blood pressure, among other things.

TIPS TO HELP YOU SLEEP

- Write down a list of all the things you have to do the following day, so that they aren't running through your mind when your head hits the pillow.
- Go to bed at the same time each night.
- Have a warm bath before bed.
- Try some gentle yoga or stretches for ten minutes.
- Play soothing music.
- Avoid watching TV or looking at your phone just before bedtime.
- Read a book for at least ten minutes before you turn off the lights.
- Have a warm milky drink before going to bed.
- Sprinkle a few drops of lavender essential oil on to a tissue and tuck it under your pillow.
- Take at least 20 minutes of energetic exercise during the day.
- Ensure that your bedroom is between 15–19°C (60–67°F) – it is always best to err on the cool side.
- Turn the clock face away from you but set an alarm. That way you won't worry about the time or the possibility of oversleeping.

SLEEPING AIDS

HOP-FILLED PILLOW

Besides their use as a key ingredient in beer, hops have traditionally been used to assist in promoting sleep. As far back as Roman times, pillows were stuffed with hops to encourage sleep. Make your own version by stitching a small hop-filled bag to tuck under your pillow.

You will need

2 square pieces of muslin, approx. 10 cm^2
Needle and thread
200 g dried hops

Method

- Stitch the two squares together around each side, leaving a small opening on one edge.
- Turn the bag inside out to hide the seams.
- Fill the bag with hops – a home-made paper funnel will help to get the hops into the pocket you've created.
- Stitch the remaining edge to make sure the contents don't spill out.
- Tuck under your pillow then enjoy a deep and dreamy sleep!

WARMING HEAT-PACK

This warming heat-pack is ideal for soothing tired muscles and aching feet, so that you can sleep soundly.

You will need

Pretty fabric
Cotton thread
Pins
Sewing machine (or you can stitch by hand with a needle)
1 kg wheat
2 tbsp dried lavender

You can use rose petals, cloves, ginger, rosemary or crushed mint as an alternative to lavender, while uncooked rice, barley or flaxseeds can be used as alternatives to wheat.

Method

- Cut out two rectangles of fabric measuring 16 x 11.5 cm. Pin the two rectangles together, patterned sides facing each other.
- Stitch around the rectangle 1 cm from the pinned edge, leaving one end open.
- Cut off the corners.
- Turn the fabric so that the right side is facing out.
- Fill with the wheat and lavender.
- Fold to form a 1-cm seam along the open end.
- Stitch the bag close to the edge and then remove the pins.
- Heat for two minutes in the microwave – always check the temperature carefully before allowing contact with your skin.

SOOTHING BEDTIME DRINKS

A warm milk drink before bed may help you sleep, as milk boosts levels of the sleep-inducing hormone melatonin. It also contains tryptophan, an amino acid that stimulates the release of serotonin, which makes you sleepy. Plus, it is high in calcium, which can help reduce stress.

MILK AND HONEY

This is the perfect bedtime drink, as it combines milk with cinnamon, which has antiviral and antifungal properties. **Serves: 1**

Ingredients

250 ml milk (or non-dairy alternative)
¼ tsp cinnamon powder
2–3 drops of vanilla essence
1 tsp agave syrup or honey

Method

- Place the milk in a pan.
- Add the cinnamon and vanilla essence, and warm over a low heat, stirring gently.
- Add the agave syrup or honey to taste.

BANANA SMOOTHIE

Perfect if you want a cool drink before bed. Bananas are said to help lift the mood and prevent muscle spasms. **Serves: 1**

Ingredients

250 ml milk (or a non-dairy alternative)
1 banana
1 tsp smooth peanut butter
1 tsp honey (or another sweetener, such as agave syrup or coconut sugar)
Ice (if required)

Method

- Pour the milk into a jug.
- Add the banana and peanut butter.
- Blend until smooth.
- Add honey and ice, as required.

OTHER DRINKS TO HELP YOU SLEEP

- Camomile tea – camomile is known for its calming and sleep-inducing effects. It has a fragrant light taste and you can sweeten it with honey, if required.
- Cherry juice – cherries are high in melatonin, which is the hormone that triggers sleep and regulates your body clock.
- Valerian root tea – it has a distinctive taste, so it is best to mix it with another tea, such as camomile or mint. It has been used for centuries as a sleeping aid.
- Blackstrap molasses – add a teaspoon to warm milk for a gingery flavour. Molasses has a calming effect on the brain and nerves.

STRETCH

It's advisable to stretch the body regularly to keep it supple, reduce stiffness, improve health and lower stress levels. It also helps to keep your joints healthy.

While it's lovely to go to a class, there are lots of simple stretches you can also do safely in the comfort of your home, whenever convenient, like these ones for your calf and lower back.

CHILD'S POSE

This is a lovely and relaxing yoga pose that is perfect for stretching out the lower back. You'll need an exercise mat or a carpeted floor.

- Kneel and push your bottom towards your heels, while stretching your arms out in front of you.
- Part your knees slightly so that your body rests in between them.
- Rest your forehead on or towards the floor (depending on your flexibility).
- Take a few deep breaths.
- Adjust your position so that you can really feel the stretch. Push your arms further forward and your bottom further back towards your heels, as you go deeper into the pose.
- Breathe deeply, as you feel the stretch in your lower back.
- If comfortable, you can stay in this position for a few minutes.

SEATED CALF STRETCH

Your calves get tight over time, when they are not being moved regularly, so if you sit at a desk from nine to five, this is recommended. Ideally, you should do it every day.

- Sit on the floor with your legs extended.
- Loop a resistance band (or a dressing-gown cord or similar) around one foot, holding both sides of it with your hands.
- Gently pull your toes towards your shin until you feel the stretch in your calf. Hold for 20 seconds and breathe deeply while you are stretching.
- This shouldn't hurt – the stretch should feel relaxing and releasing. If there is any pain, loosen the band.
- Repeat on the other side.
- Do this twice for each leg.

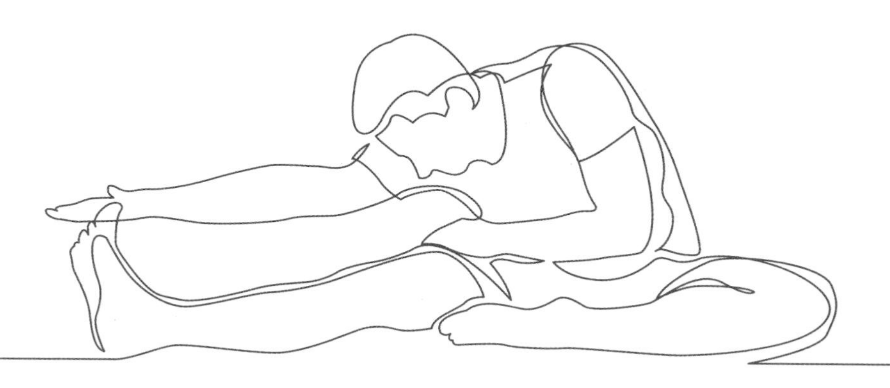

MASSAGE

While it's relaxing to have a massage by a qualified professional, there are some techniques which you can try at home to relax and ease tension.

When it comes to self-massage, one of the handiest things you can own is a tennis ball (make sure it's a firm one).

Try these easy shoulder and foot massages.

SHOULDER MASSAGE

- Take a tennis ball and hold it against the wall with your shoulder.
- Roll your shoulder over the tennis ball, pushing into any areas that are knotted with tension. Take deep breaths as you do this; it shouldn't hurt.
- Repeat on the other shoulder.

FOOT MASSAGE

- First, prepare your oil. Use 12 drops of peppermint oil to every 30 ml of carrier oil – sweet almond oil is lovely, but you can also use a simple vegetable oil.
- Find a comfortable position, and use a towel to protect furnishings and clothes.
- Warm the mixed oil in your hands and rub it into your feet, concentrating on any sore or tight areas.
- If you feel pain, be very gentle. Also, make sure that you work gently in between the toes.

If you want to work with some of the acupoints (these are energy points linked to other areas of the body) in your feet then you could invest in a reflexology map, as this will show you where to apply pressure in order to benefit certain parts of the body. Acupressure is always best done professionally, but if you are gentle, you won't cause any harm by having a go yourself. Be careful with any painful areas.

BREATHING

The breath is a powerful tool and, considering we do it 24/7, it might be shocking to discover that most of us aren't breathing properly. We take short breaths and hold the air in when we are anxious or get into the habit of shallow breathing because we are under constant stress. Plus, we spend too long sitting down, which squashes the lower lobes of our lungs and means we don't get rid of many of the toxins we breathe in.

Shallow breathing pushes you into fight-or-flight mode – the heart rate increases, blood pressure goes up and your body becomes ready for attack. This is handy if you are being chased by a lion, but in ordinary, everyday life it's not good for the body. It's particularly difficult to digest food while in this state, as blood from the gut is diverted to the brain and muscles in readiness for a fight.

The mind and the breath are profoundly connected and this is why breathing is an intrinsic part of yoga. You'll notice that your breathing quickens in times of stress and slows when you are relaxed. Therefore, you will start to feel calmer if you focus on your breathing, and deliberately attempt to slow it down and take deeper lungfuls of air. When you do this, the heart rate slows, the blood pressure lowers and the body is allowed to rest, which is why breathing properly is an effective stress reliever.

By incorporating a short daily breathing practice into your life, you can expect some of these benefits:

- Reduced stress and anxiety
- The ability to better regulate your emotions
- A body that heals better
- A longer lifespan
- Feeling calmer
- Better posture
- Stronger lungs
- A higher pain threshold

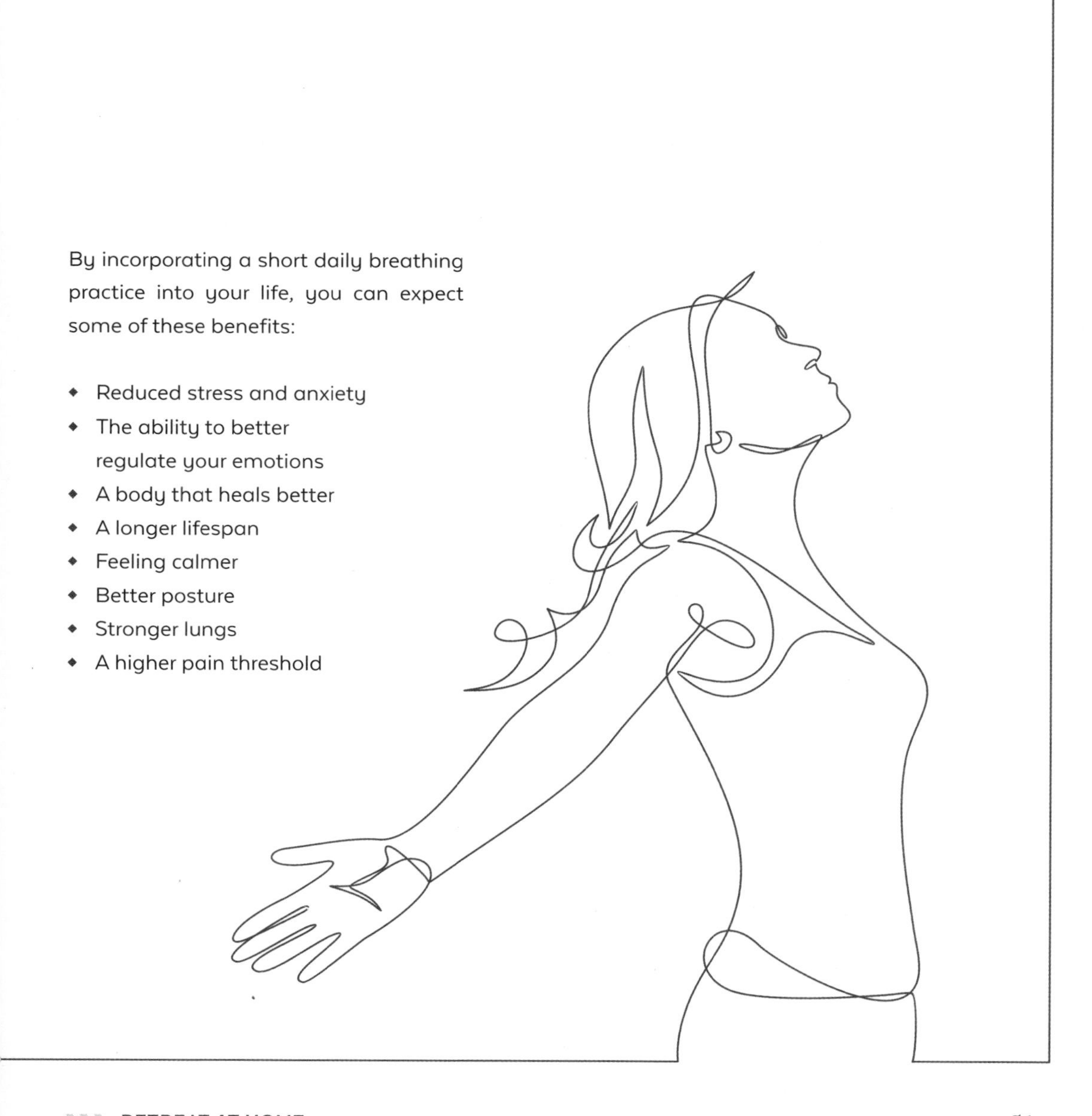

BREATHING EXERCISES

Try to do at least one breathing exercise daily. It doesn't need to take up a lot of time – and besides, you breathe every minute of the day anyway!

If you have never done any breathing exercises before, start off with belly breathing, which is both easy to do and very relaxing.

BELLY BREATHING

- Sit or lie flat in a comfortable position.
- Put one hand on your stomach, just below your ribs, and the other on your chest.
- Take a deep breath through the nose and, as you do so, allow your stomach to push your hand out. Your chest should not move.
- Breathe out through pursed lips, using the hand on your tummy to gently expel the air.
- Repeat three to ten times.

THREE-MINUTE BOX BREATHING

This is a powerful stress reliever.

- Breathe in through the nose over a count of five then hold the breath for five and exhale through the mouth for five. This will take a bit of getting used to at first.
- Repeat for at least three minutes.
- Aim to do this a few times throughout the day, if possible.

CALMING BREATHING

If you feel panicky or notice that your breath is particularly shallow, try breathing in through the nose for seven counts and, without holding your breath at all, exhale through the mouth for nine counts.

FOCUSED BREATHING EXERCISE

This yogic technique focuses the mind and is ideal just before you sit down to meditate.

- Take a deep breath in through the nose.
- Breathe out in six to ten short outbursts of air through your nostrils. You'll notice your stomach contract as you do this.
- Repeat three times.

ONLINE RETREATS

There's a wealth of online courses and classes that allow you to work with some of the best therapists and retreat facilitators from all over the world, using your computer, laptop, mobile phone or smart device. Some even hold online half- or full-day retreats with live video streaming, which you can follow in your own home.

You can either participate on your own or as part of an online community, as going on retreat does not always mean spending time in solitude. Many of the platforms, like Zoom, used for holding workshops and classes feature breakout rooms where people are divided into small groups to share their experiences with others (if they feel comfortable doing that).

The best way to find the right online facilitator for you is to have a good search online. Decide what it is you want to do and bear in mind that there are workshops and retreats for just about anything, whether it be getting rich, dealing with stress or learning how to dance. Also, check out any YouTube videos the facilitator has made to see if you like their style of teaching before signing up.

Some therapists will allow a short preliminary phone call to see if you get along. Many of the online tutors and coaches have Facebook groups, so you can chat to others in their community to find out if they are a good fit for you. It's always best to see if you can do a free taster session before you part with any cash, because sometimes it can take time to find the right coach. What works for one person may leave another cold.

Think big. Check out the therapists and teachers who have written books you admire. It doesn't matter where they are based and you'll find that online retreats cost less than the physical variety, meaning you may well be able to afford the best!

If you do book an online course, make sure you are prepared in advance. So if you've booked yoga, have a mat, props, suitable clothes and enough space to do all the poses. If you are doing a silent retreat or something that involves meditation and quiet contemplation, ensure that you've prewarned family and friends, put a sign on your door and have all that you need to make yourself comfortable.

F11
F12

RETREAT REFRESHMENTS

It will do wonders for your health if you stick to light, nutritious snacks and healthy drinks during retreat time. Consuming the best foods you can lay your hands on will support the process as it works its magic on your mind, body and soul.

Processed foods should be avoided during your retreat experience, although a few squares of dark chocolate containing 70 per cent or more cocoa solids, or some cacao nibs, are good for you and can improve your mood.

If you like to snack throughout the day, try preparing healthier versions of your favourites.

Here are some easy swaps to make:

- Crisps – swap them for popcorn kernels that you cook yourself and season with your favourite spices. Paprika is delicious on popcorn; salt and pepper also work well, and you can add fresh ingredients too, such as chopped chives.
- Bread – whether it's white, brown or sourdough, bread can make you feel sluggish. Try rye, spelt or oat crackers instead, as they're lighter to digest.
- Cake – for those sweet cravings, make your own ice-cream treats by slicing a banana, dipping half of each slice into melted dark chocolate and

freezing on a sheet of greaseproof paper. Or, for something even sweeter, halve a whole date and remove the stone, fill the centre with your favourite nut butter, coat with melted dark chocolate and cool in the fridge.

- Fizzy drinks – forget them while you are on retreat and drink water instead. Make a jug of water more interesting by adding mint leaves, slices of cucumber, orange, apple, etc. Do this an hour or so before you drink it to allow the flavours to infuse.
- Tea and coffee – fruit and herbal teas (plus decaffeinated tea and coffee) will prove more soothing for you than drinks that contain caffeine.
- Biscuits – hide the tin and try dipping some crackers into your favourite nut butter instead.
- Sweets – give them a miss and try freezing whole or halved grapes. They make a delicious cooling snack, ideal for the summer months.

HEALTHY RECIPES

Savour these healthy and delicious recipes any day of the week, but especially when you are on retreat.

You can either make them on the day or prepare them beforehand. The soup can be stored in the freezer in batches and defrosted when you need it.

BUTTERNUT SQUASH SOUP

This is an easy-to-make, flavoursome soup, ideal for lunch, supper or a mid-afternoon snack. **Serves: 2**

Ingredients

1 onion, sliced
½ a butternut squash, peeled and cubed
2 carrots, peeled and cubed
½ litre vegetable bouillon
1 tsp turmeric powder
Salt
Pepper

Method

- Fry the onion and butternut squash in a large saucepan until they turn brown and sticky.
- Add the carrots and turmeric powder, and fry for two minutes.
- Pour in the vegetable bouillon and simmer until the squash and carrots are soft.
- Blend the mixture until smooth.
- Season to taste.
- Serve hot with some sourdough or rye bread. You could add a swirl of sour cream or yogurt, if desired.

BERRY BANANA SMOOTHIE

This smoothie is a delicious and nutritious breakfast drink. **Serves: 1**

Ingredients

½ mug mixed berries
1 medium banana
2 tbsp jumbo oats
2 tsp cashew nut butter
2 tsp mixed seeds – chia, sunflower, sesame, flax, etc.
Splash of plant-based milk, if needed

Method

- Put all the ingredients into a blender and blend until smooth. Add in a splash of plant-based milk if the mixture doesn't easily blend, or if you prefer a thinner consistency.
- Pour into a tall glass and enjoy!

TUNA LETTUCE WRAPS

These make a tasty lunch or supper. They're light, nutritious and easy to prepare. **Serves: 2**

Ingredients

1 avocado
½ tsp mustard powder
1 tsp apple cider vinegar
1 tsp capers
8 romaine lettuce leaves
1 small can of tuna, drained
16 cherry tomatoes, halved

Method

- Halve and stone the avocado, then scoop out the flesh.
- Add the mustard and vinegar to the avocado then mash together.
- Stir in the capers.
- Spoon the mixture on to the lettuce leaves.
- Add the tuna and cherry tomatoes.
- Roll into little wraps.

IMMUNE BOOSTERS

In order for your body to function at its absolute best, keep its natural defences in tip-top condition by boosting your immune system whenever possible and consuming the right nutrients.

Try these simple immune-boosting recipes!

TURMERIC TEA

Turmeric, with its naturally vibrant yellow colour, has antioxidant, antibacterial, antiviral and anti-inflammatory properties, which can boost the body's immune system. Turmeric tea is one of the most effective and easiest ways of consuming the spice. Follow this simple recipe to make a relaxing, warming cup. **Serves: 1**

Ingredients

1 tsp fresh or dried turmeric root, grated*

250 ml of hot water

Method

- Simply allow the spice to steep in hot water and then sip as desired.
- You can also prepare large quantities, allowing the tea a longer period to brew. Store this in the fridge and reheat the required amount in a pan.

** If you can't find turmeric root, the powdered variety can be used instead.*

IMMUNE-BOOSTER SHOT

This easy-to-make immune-booster shot can help stave off colds. **Serves: 1**

Ingredients

1 tsp honey
½ tsp turmeric powder
60 ml hot water
Juice of half a lemon
Juice of 1 orange
1 tsp apple cider vinegar

Method

- Stir the honey and turmeric into the hot water with a spoon until they dissolve.
- Add the lemon and orange juices, and the apple cider vinegar.
- Stir and drink.

PART TWO

RETREAT TO NATURE

Spending time close to nature is good for your health, happiness and soul because we are part of its rhythms and cycles.

An American study found that those who take regular walks in nature do 20 per cent better in memory tests, while a Finnish survey found that spending just 15 minutes in nature helps people feel happier.

Our bodies need time outdoors to create vitamin D, which can help prevent cancer, osteoporosis and heart attacks; also, research has shown that patients who are exposed to natural light heal faster and have less pain following surgery.

It's not a cure-all, but if you spend at least some time every day close to nature – even if it's just a short walk through the local park or admiring a pretty flower – you'll feel happier and healthier.

A GARDEN SANCTUARY

If you are lucky enough to have access to a garden, it will make the ideal outdoor sanctuary for all kinds of retreat activities – from quiet contemplation through to yoga, stretching, gardening or dozing off in the sunshine.

As with your home, it's going to help hugely if you make the space as comfortable and pleasing to the eye as possible.

Give the place a tidy-up if you haven't done so already and plant things that you love, checking first that you are providing the perfect growing conditions, as certain plants prefer the shade, some like full sunshine and many thrive in a well-drained soil (that doesn't get waterlogged in the rain). It will save a lot of work if you put things in the right place and the correct distance from other plants to begin with. If you don't have flower beds, you can always use ceramic pots – and if you love bees or butterflies, consider choosing plants that attract them.

Here are a few examples of plants that bees and butterflies flock to:

- Chrysanthemum
- Winter aconite
- Lavender
- Geranium
- Buddleia
- Sedum

NB never use pesticides on plants in bloom, as this will repel the insects.

PLANNING YOUR GARDEN

Sketch a quick plan of your garden before you buy anything and start planting. Work out if you need a vegetable patch, where the best places to sit are, and where items such as your washing line and bins will be positioned.

Garden furniture needn't be lavish, but you will need somewhere to sit in a shady spot, so choose either a bench or a comfortable chair. A table will prove useful, too. If you can, have something portable that you can move into the sunshine as you wish or invest in a recliner. If you have trees, why not consider a hammock – there are few things more relaxing than gently swaying as you read. Add some scatter cushions that you can take indoors overnight and when it rains.

Think of your garden as you would a room and consider adding some special touches that will make it all the more appealing – pretty fairy lights, a linen tablecloth, a weatherproof beanbag, lanterns, etc. If there are any unsightly areas where you store bins, recycling boxes or a bicycle, try to position them behind some screening. You can also use climbing plants and trellis to hide things that you would rather not see. Mosaics are an attractive decoration for a garden, while mirrors make it look bigger.

A water feature is a lovely addition, as the sound is so soothing. You don't have to spend a lot of money to find something that will burble away in a corner of your garden and make you feel as if you were close to a brook. If a water feature is out of the question, try a birdbath instead. Keep it filled with fresh water and you can admire visiting birds as they splash about.

GARDENING

If you've never turned your hand to gardening before then you are missing out – being outdoors with your hands in the soil, watching things grow, is perfect for calming a hectic mind.

You can start small with some seeds grown on a windowsill. Cultivating herbs in pots is a nice introduction to growing things and many are hardier than most houseplants. If they are close to your eyeline in the kitchen, you should remember to water them daily and, of course, they are always on hand to flavour your food. Once you've tried fresh herbs you've grown yourself, you'll never want to go back to the dried shop-bought variety!

If you have space, try growing vegetables in pots. Here are some that don't require an allotment or a big garden:

- Tomatoes – as long as they are watered and in well-drained soil, you can grow them in a bag of compost. You'll be amazed at how many fruits are produced over the summer.
- Swiss chard – with its red and yellow stems, and deep green leaves, chard grows well in pots on a patio or balcony.
- Kale – packed with vitamins, it grows nicely in a pot, as long as it is protected from the wind.
- Lettuce – with its shallow root system, lettuce is ideal for growing in limited spaces where there's plenty of shade.

And if veg isn't your bag, try these easy-to-grow flowers:

- Sunflowers – water them well and give them sunlight, and they could grow taller than you.
- Daffodils – plant in a rich, well-drained soil and they will create a brilliant display come springtime.
- Impatiens – the perfect plant for beginners. They will come up every year, and tolerate shade; also, they are cheap to buy. Have fun with them!

WHAT IS A SENSORY GARDEN?

A sensory garden includes plants, features, surfaces and objects that stimulate the senses and transform an outside space into a therapeutic and restful spot. Even if you only have a small balcony, you can turn it into a glorious sensory experience.

How you design your sensory garden depends on what you will be using it for – a place where the kids will be entertained, a healing oasis or somewhere that achieves a bit of both.

The trick is to blend elements such as benches, paths, water features and birdbaths into the shape of the garden to enhance the design, and then fill it with plants and items that play with all the senses.

A sensory space is an interactive one, so try to avoid spiky or poisonous plants. Choose things that you can reach out and pick, such as rosemary for cooking and blooms that smell wonderful and can be placed in vases indoors. Consider the height of plants lining any areas where you will walk, as they'll need to be within grasping distance if you want to reach out and touch them.

During the planning stage, ensure that there are spots of interest and colour in the garden all year round. And don't just use plants for colour: consider the shades of decking, bricks and stone. You can paint fencing and walls, or use mirrors to reflect light and make the garden seem bigger. Think about introducing interesting pots and perhaps some stones, gravel or bark, plus unique ornaments or sculptures.

Like your home, the garden should reflect who you are. If you like bold decorations, go wild; if you are someone who prefers minimalist decor, reflect that in the way you design your garden. It's your space and you should feel soothed the moment you set foot in it.

CREATE A SENSORY GARDEN

Creating your own sensory garden will provide pleasure all round. The smells, sights, sounds, sensations and tastes will make it a place you never want to leave. You don't need a huge amount of space – a small balcony is enough to create a zone where all your senses can be stimulated.

***Touch:** there are lots of plants that cry out to be handled, thanks to their interesting textures. Lamb's ear is baby-soft, moss feels cool and springy, and running your fingers over a lavender bush is irresistible. Bark has a stimulating texture, Cape sundew is an interesting sticky plant that eats insects, and yarrow has stiff flowers and soft foliage. Think about texture underfoot, too – you could use tiles, gravel, grass or a mixture of different surfaces. Remember, the garden has to be both practical and enjoyable, so if you hate the idea of having to mow the lawn every week, opt for a hard surface.*

Taste: *add some edible fruits like trailing strawberries, herbs such as basil and parsley, and vegetables, many of which can be grown in pots if you don't have much space (see page 69). You could also include edible flowers, such as nasturtiums and pansies.*

Sight: *design your garden to be both interesting and beautiful. Mix trailing plants with shrubs and delicate flowers. Aim to create a balance between vibrant colours and relaxing, soft hues to avoid overstimulation. Ceramic pots come in a huge variety of tones and you can also add colour with a shade (such as a parasol), garden furniture, painted walls and sheds, etc.*

Smell: *fill your garden with heavenly scents that will help to soothe and calm. Choose plants such as lavender, honeysuckle, jasmine and herbs. Some varieties of rose create a wondrous fragrance, while others barely smell at all, so make sure you do your research. It is best to pick some flowering plants when they are in bloom, so you can have a good sniff at the garden centre.*

Sound: *wind chimes, bells and water features all provide relaxing sounds, but you could also opt for ornamental grasses and trees with leaves that whisper in the wind, such as silver birch, willow and eucalyptus.*

THE BEAUTY OF BIRDS

Many of us go about our business without noticing the layers of birdsong that fill the air or the many different species that inhabit our towns, countryside and gardens. Pay attention to birds and you will notice an inspiring world that you always have access to.

If you've ever wondered why birdwatchers spend hours hiding in the bushes, looking at their favourite species, try admiring our feathered friends yourself. If you have a garden, it's worth investing in a bird feeder, nesting box or bath, which will attract many of the common species found in your area.

Birds are delicate, beautiful and fascinating, and if you watch them closely, you'll be so transfixed that worries, pressing thoughts and to-do lists will no longer be a concern.

The more you look at birds, the better your observation skills will become and you'll start to notice variations in their plumage, the quality of their calls and interesting behaviours. There is always something new to learn when you watch birds. If you really get into this hobby, it might be worth investing in some binoculars and a field guide to common species.

COMMON BIRD SPECIES

- Robin – one of the easiest birds to spot thanks to its bright red chest. They're an inquisitive species and will often investigate when you are gardening, in the hope that you'll dig up some tasty worms or bugs in the soil.
- Goldfinch – a vibrant bird with a red face and yellow streak on its wings that has a peaceful, twittering song. They migrate to warmer climates in the winter, but are common in cooler European countries in the spring and summer months.
- Wood pigeon – a plump grey shimmering bird with a soft cooing song; it makes a ruffling sound with its wings when it takes off.
- Blackbird – the males are black with orange beaks, while the females are brown with white spots. They have a restful mellow song.
- House sparrow – found all over the world, this bird has brown and grey plumage, and an incessant chirping call.
- Wren – one of the most common birds in Europe, this is a small brown bird that likes to hide, yet has a very loud song. Species in the Americas are even smaller.

BIRDSEED CAKE

If you want to attract more birds into your garden or even on to a balcony, try making this easy birdseed cake. The birds will love you for it, especially during the winter months when the ground is frozen and it's harder for them to find food. It's also great for the springtime, when they need a lot of extra energy to feed their growing chicks.

The basis for this recipe is fat, which birds love; for the filling you don't necessarily have to go to the shops, as you can use scraps, such as cheese or dry porridge oats.

You will need

Unsalted peanuts
Sunflower seeds
Currants
Sultanas
Oats
Breadcrumbs
Cake crumbs
Grated cheese
Lard or suet (use one-part fat to three-parts dry mixture)
Empty yogurt pots
String

Method

- Mix your dry ingredients in a bowl.
- Melt some lard or suet in a pan and add it to the dry mixture, so that the fat is absorbed and it all sticks together.
- Make a hole in the bottom of the yogurt pot and thread a length of string through it – this will run through the mix, rather like a wick does in a candle.
- Spoon the fatty mixture into the yogurt pot, filling it to the top and making sure the string is in the centre.
- Place in the fridge.
- When set, cut the pot away and hang the block on a tree or shrub, and wait for the birds to feast on it.

You can store these seed cakes in the freezer. Never put them out on hot summer days, as the sun will melt the fat and this could be dangerous if it gets on to the birds' plumage. If you want an easier method, fill small terracotta plant posts with raw peanuts, seeds, breadcrumbs, etc. and keep them topped up all-year round. Hang them in trees so the foxes won't get them. You can also attract birds by growing seed-producing plants, such as sunflowers, and plants with berries, such as holly, rowan and cotoneaster.

GET IN TOUCH WITH NATURE

You don't have to trek for miles or find somewhere wild and remote: nature is within reach for most of us. Walking in a local park or along a tree-lined avenue, or even picking daisies from a patch of grass, will help you to feel connected to nature.

Being in nature soothes our sympathetic nervous system, which is associated with threat, while activating the parasympathetic nervous system, which is associated with peacefulness and calm.

DAILY NATURE CHALLENGE

- Make a point of noticing three wonderful things in nature – anything from the colour of the leaves when the sun shines on them to birdsong or the scent of a flower – and write them down.
- This will help to deepen your connection to and appreciation for the natural world. You can look at your jottings whenever you feel low, as a way to remember all the wonderful things you've seen.
- Notice if, after doing this exercise daily, your mood improves over time.

FOR THE LOVE OF TREES

Remember how much fun you had with trees as a kid – climbing them, making dens and forming pretty patterns with the autumn leaves? Rekindle that wonder and take a little time to appreciate the trees that surround you. They are one of the most awe-inspiring features of the natural world.

APPRECIATE THE MAGNIFICENCE OF TREES

- Take a long, hard look at a tree: observe its size and shape.
- Look up to the treetop.
- Notice the leaves. Look closer and observe the pattern on their surface.
- Touch the bark.
- Picture the tree as a young sapling and imagine the years it has taken to grow to its current size.
- Think about how its roots are spread out beneath your feet – did you know that in a forest, healthy trees will pass nutrients to sick trees through their root system?

NATURE MEDITATION

SIMPLE NATURE MEDITATION

Meditating outdoors, close to nature, can be relaxing, inspiring and healing. It will give you a boost if you manage to do it regularly, as research has shown that green spaces are mood-enhancing.

It's as simple as sitting on a park bench somewhere quiet, where you can hear the wind in the trees and the birds singing. You could find a spot in the countryside, on a beach or even in your own garden. As long as nature is close by and it is peaceful, you will feel wonderfully soothed by being outdoors among trees, plants, birds and animals.

We are part of the natural world, but in our busy, frenetic lives we tend to forget that. Being in nature reminds us to slow down. You only have to look around to appreciate that nature has its own easy-going pace. It doesn't rush or fret; it does what it is supposed to do in its own good time.

- Find a place outdoors to sit comfortably.
- Take three deep breaths and become aware of your body. Feel the grass or bench beneath you and do a quick body scan from your toes to the top of your head. If you can, take off your shoes and socks, and touch the grass beneath your feet.
- Keep your eyes open and look at the nature around you. Really appreciate its beauty.
- Feel the sun/breeze/cold/warmth on your face.
- Listen to the sounds of nature – the birds, the rustle of leaves, the creaking of trees.
- Appreciate your own connection to the natural world. You are a part of nature, just like the things you've been observing.
- Breathe slowly and deeply. Continue to take in your surroundings. If your thoughts run away with you, bring yourself back to your breathing.
- If you like, you can then deepen this meditation by closing your eyes. There is no time limit to this, but it's best to do this for at least ten minutes.

WALKING MEDITATION

You can also try meditating while walking. This can happen anywhere, but it is particularly good when done close to nature. For Buddhist monks, walking is an essential part of their practice and they often do it for as long as 15 hours a day. There is no need to match the Buddhist monks – ten minutes spent walking in nature is enough for a deep and relaxing experience.

A walking meditation asks that you pay close attention to every movement. You should be engrossed in the walking and not thinking about other things. Your mind may wander, but when it does, gently bring your attention back to your movements. It takes some practice, but once you have mastered it, walking meditation clears the mind, reduces stress and can create a feeling of inner calm.

SIMPLE WALKING MEDITATION

- Choose a secluded, pretty spot: you are going to walk back and forth on the same path, so that you don't have to think too hard.
- Take three deep breaths and pay attention to the sensation of your feet on the ground.
- Start to walk slowly, at least half your normal pace. As you move, place all of your attention on the soles of your feet.
- Walk back and forth along the same short stretch, not looking at anything in particular.
- If your mind wanders, bring your attention back to the sensations and motion of your feet.
- If at any time you feel like standing still or sitting, then do so.
- If something beautiful catches your eye, stop to look at it.
- There is no "correct" experience. Just keep walking and if any difficult emotions surface, allow them to pass through.
- As you walk, enjoy every step you take and feel gratitude for the natural world around you.

JOGGING

Jogging through your favourite beauty spots can be as relaxing as walking, once your body is used to it. You'll burn up more calories and the endorphin hit at the end of a run will leave you on a high long after you've cooled down.

If you are new to running, take it easy: if you tackle too much too soon, you risk an injury. A good way to start is by going on a walk-run. If you are an absolute beginner, start by walking briskly for five minutes and running slowly for two; then go back to the walking and repeat. You should be able to hold a conversation while doing a gentle jog.

If you increase the amount of time spent running each week, your body will grow accustomed to it and you will start to feel more comfortable.

It can be a good idea to find a running buddy: somebody who is at the same ability level and who can jog alongside you. Chatting to a friend will take your mind off the ache in your limbs.

If you think running feels challenging, take a look at some of the regular joggers where you live. Can you see that most of them look relaxed, as if they could go on forever? That could be you, if you keep going.

MEXICAN HOT CHOCOLATE

This hot drink is ideal for your cool-down period. Chocolate helps to boost blood flow, cayenne speeds up metabolism and milk will help the muscles recover. **Serves: 1**

Ingredients

250 ml low-fat milk (or a non-dairy alternative)
30 g 70% dark chocolate, grated or chopped
2 tsp honey (or agave syrup or coconut sugar)
1 drop of vanilla essence
1 pinch of cayenne pepper

Method

- Heat the milk in a pan and stir in the chocolate until melted.
- Add the honey to sweeten.
- Add the vanilla and cayenne pepper to taste.

FOREST BATHING

"Forest bathing" is a term used to describe the act of immersing yourself in a forest setting as a way to step out of the busy world and calm the mind. It originated in Japan, where it is called *shinrin-yoku* and seen as an essential component of the healthcare system. It was promoted to ease the stress levels of city workers, as well as helping them to reconnect with nature and fall in love with the country's forests, so that they would be more likely to want to protect them.

Studies have shown that forest bathing reduces stress, is good for mental health and boosts the immune system – plus, it can accelerate recovery from an illness. It also sharpens the mind, sparks creativity and aids restful sleep.

Forest bathing is much more than simply going to the woods: the idea is that you use mindfulness and meditation techniques to connect with your surroundings.

FOREST-BATHING GUIDE

Create your own forest-bathing experience with this easy guide:

- Find a nearby forest and allow yourself at least two hours to spend among the trees.
- Remember to wear comfortable foot wear, outdoor clothing and sun-screen (if necessary).
- Turn your phone off when you get to your location.
- Enter the forest and stand still in one spot.
- Fully immerse yourself in the environment. Feel your feet on the forest floor; take note of any smells, the breeze on your skin and the sounds. Savour your surroundings.
- Take a leaf from a tree and look at it closely. Appreciate its intricacy.
- Move through the forest, wherever your feet want to take you. Walk slowly and mindfully, and breathe deeply.
- Pay close attention to any trees that catch your eye. Smell them up close – certain tree aromas, such as cedar and birch, are said to boost the immune system. Roll the sap between your thumb and forefinger, if there is any oozing from the bark, or roll the leaves in your hands until their scent is released.
- Find a comfortable spot and sit quietly for at least ten minutes. Breathe deeply and listen to the sounds of the forest.
- If your mind wanders, bring yourself back to your breath or the forest sounds.
- If the weather permits, it can be soothing to lie on the forest floor and look up at the treetops.
- Traditionally, Japanese forest-bathing sessions end with a tea ceremony, a time to reflect on all you experienced in the forest – you could recreate this by bringing along with you a flask of tea or another drink.

GO WILD

There's nothing quite like going off the beaten track and spending time somewhere remote and wild, where you might find that you are the only person for miles. It's so good for your well-being, in fact, that many places now offer "wilderness therapy" – using adventure activities as a therapeutic process. Participants learn how to survive in the wild, which gives them the confidence to face the challenges in their everyday life.

It's not necessary to go on an organized programme to reap the benefits of time in the wilderness. All you need to do is plan a trip (make sure you are prepared and have everything you require) and go somewhere remote. If you live in an urban area, prepare to journey out of town, and choose a destination that you know you will love – the beach, the woods, mountains, hills, river, etc.

To get the most out of going wild, attempt to stay overnight, although it's not a must. You can either camp or find a place to stay that gives you both access to the wilderness and somewhere warm and comfortable to retreat to at the end of the day. Just make sure you have the relevant permissions to set up camp in the location you choose.

When you venture into the wilderness, ensure that you carry a rucksack containing everything you'll need for the day – and night, if you are camping. You'll get more out of the experience if you prepare your beverages and meals outdoors: a small gas stove, and some tin cups and pans are easily portable.

There are no rules, so just do whatever takes your fancy, but do aim to take in the views, the smells, colours and sounds. Take a mental photograph of the wilderness, as you might like to visualize it when you feel stressed, once you're back to everyday life.

Do take a mobile phone and battery charger in a waterproof bag, just in case you get into trouble, and let others know where you are going before you set off. Also, always take a bottle of drinking water.

POCKET-SIZED WILDERNESS SURVIVAL KIT

You'll need a small tin and something waterproof to keep it in.

- Plasters
- Painkillers
- Lighter
- Water-purifying tablets
- A small whistle (to get attention if you become lost and don't have a phone signal)
- A penknife
- Compass

FORAGING

Foraging for food in the wild is fun and satisfying – knowing that nature provides everything you need for free is a rewarding experience. The woods, hedgerows and fields are filled with ingredients that can make some fantastic dishes.

Before you go foraging, make sure it is allowed at the places you are visiting; never eat wild mushrooms or fungi, unless you can confidently identify them, and only take from places where supplies are plentiful – wildlife depends on these foods, too!

You cannot rush when you go foraging. The key is to move slowly and be aware of your surroundings – move too quickly and you might miss some delicious treasures.

If you are serious about it, your finds will supplement your supermarket shop. Foraging was a way of life for our ancestors and if you look carefully, you'll come across a wide range of foods, including nettles, berries, fruits and nuts. Always make sure you wash your finds thoroughly before consuming them. The following page includes ideas for foods you might be able to forage locally.

***Nettles** – make sure you wear gloves to pick these or else they will sting you. Pick the pale, green nettle tops but never when they are in flower, as they'll be tough and woody. Early spring is the best time to gather nettles. Use them in soups, stews and pies. Once cooked, they don't sting any more.*

***Sloes** – from September to November, hedgerows are bursting with plump, purple sloe berries. Try making them into jam or infuse them with gin or vodka for a tasty Christmas tipple.*

***Blackberries** – found in the autumn hedgerows, they go well with apples and make a delicious jam.*

***Wild garlic** – you will find this close to streams and rivers. Pick the young leaves from March onwards and use the little white flowers to flavour salads.*

***Sweet chestnuts** – another autumnal find. They are delicious roasted on their own or added to pasta and stir-fries.*

FORAGING RECIPES

Once you've been out foraging, try these easy recipes. **Makes: 1 jar**

WILD GARLIC MAYONNAISE

Wild garlic is a bulbous plant that grows in damp woodlands.

Ingredients

90 g wild garlic
Salt
450 ml rapeseed oil
3 egg yolks
1 tsp smooth mustard
2 tsp white wine vinegar

Method

- Rinse the wild garlic and immerse it in salted boiling water for 35 seconds.
- Drain, plunge into cold water and pat dry.
- Chop the garlic and place in a blender.
- Add the rapeseed oil gradually, increasing the blender's speed as you add more, until the mixture is a bright, vibrant green.
- Whisk the egg yolks, mustard and vinegar until smooth, pouring in the wild garlic oil gradually, as you whisk.
- When it is at a thick mayonnaise-like consistency, it's ready to serve. Season to taste.

DANDELION AND ORANGE BISCUITS

Dandelions are yellow flowers that thrive anywhere where there is enough sun – they're common on lawns, grasslands, meadows and at the edges of forests.
Makes: 12 biscuits

Ingredients

20 dandelion flowers
125 g softened butter
100 g caster sugar
1 egg
Zest of 1 orange, plus 1 tbsp of its juice
180 g plain flour
20 g cornflour
¼ tsp baking powder
Pinch of salt

Method

- Wash the dandelions and remove the petals, setting them aside.
- Cream the sugar and butter.
- Add the egg and orange zest.
- Sift the dry ingredients into the wet mix, then add the orange juice and dandelion petals.
- Bake for 12 minutes at 180°C/350°F.
- Cool on a wire rack and enjoy.

HIT THE BEACH

Everybody loves going to the beach and studies show that it has health benefits, too – it encourages relaxation and reduces stress levels. There's nothing quite like the sound of the waves lapping the shore to give a sensation of calm.

Researchers in Spain discovered that visiting blue space, such as oceans, rivers and lakes, has an even greater positive effect on people than green spaces do. The air is cleaner on the coast and charged with negative ions that allow the lungs to absorb more oxygen.

Don't forget to make the most of the sea and take a swim (applying waterproof sunscreen first). It is a great form of aerobic exercise, which is easy on the joints. Also, seawater is antiseptic and contains minerals that are said to help the body fight infection. Plus, it contains iodine, which is absorbed by the body as you swim; this keeps your metabolism running at an optimum rate, encourages hair and nail growth, and regulates hormones.

After your swim, try exfoliating with a handful of wet sand. Rub it over the skin vigorously and rinse off – it will slough away any dead skin cells. Make sure you reapply sunscreen afterwards. This method is particularly good for the feet, which tend to build up areas of dry skin.

By all means, relax on a towel and enjoy a snooze, but try to get moving, too, because you get a better workout when walking or running on sand. This is because your feet sink into it with every step, meaning you need to exert more energy than you would if you were driving forward off a hard surface. It's worth it, though, as the sensation of sand on bare feet is heavenly.

The good news is that after a day on the beach, you are sure to get a good night's sleep, thanks to all that fresh sea air and the effect that the sun has on lowering stress levels and regulating hormones.

BEACH ACTIVITIES

The beach is a great place to relax and take a swim, but you can really make a retreat day out of it by mixing in some other activities.

MAKE A PEBBLE SCULPTURE

When you pile pebbles on top of one another, they seem to defy gravity and can balance in unexpected ways. Unleash your creativity by making a pebble sculpture.

Method

- Use a flat rock as a base.
- Pile some sand on it before you start work.
- Balance a pebble on top of the sand – it can be any shape but there must be an area of flat surface on the top of it.
- Blow away the sand in between the pebble and the base.
- Pile some more sand on top of the pebble you have just laid.
- Stack another pebble on top, blow away the sand and keep going like this until you achieve an eye-catching shape.
- If it all tumbles down, start again. And if you are with a friend, why not have a contest to see who can build the tallest rock sculpture?

GET CREATIVE

Remember how you spent hours building sandcastles as a kid? There's no reason why you can't have as much fun as an adult. Try these activities:

- Build things and sculpt wet sand – don't be embarrassed about playing with a bucket and spade just because you're a grown-up!
- Investigate rock pools (make sure your shoes have non-slip soles).
- Play with a beach ball or Frisbee, if you are with others.
- Cook sausages over a portable barbecue or camping stove (though make sure there are no restrictions on this at your chosen location).
- Collect shells or unusual stones.
- Try some beachcombing: trawl the beach to see what you can find. Is there some attractive driftwood you can take home? Pieces of glass that have been polished by the sand and look like jewels? If you find enough interesting items, consider decorating a picture frame or creating a collage, when you get home.
- Take a walk on the beach at night. Look up at the stars, admire the moon's reflection in the water and feel the sand between your toes, immersing yourself in the magic of the coast.

UNDER THE STARS

Looking up at the sky on a clear night can help to shift your perspective. Often, problems that seem insurmountable don't feel quite so pressing when you gaze at the stars and realize just how vast the universe is.

Lying down and looking up at the night sky is also incredibly meditative, as there is little to distract you visually when it's dark. If you look carefully, you'll be able to spot some of the constellations in our galaxy, and if you're lucky, you might just catch a shooting star.

Stargazing is best done in a location where light pollution is minimal, but sometimes, on a really clear night, you get a great view of the stars even in an urban setting.

All you need is a sheet of plastic (condensation can make the ground damp at night) and a comfortable mat, a cushion and warm clothes – the temperature drops at night, so make sure you have thick socks, a hat, gloves and a blanket, if required.

For retreat purposes, you won't be using a telescope or any other device to magnify the night sky: the trick is to immerse yourself in what you can see unaided. Your eyes will adjust to the light, so stick with it and you'll be amazed by how much you can see.

If you really want to get serious about it, buy a star chart and see if you can spot some of the mapped constellations. All you really need, though, are your eyes and your imagination. To find out more about the night skies, there are plenty of books and online blogs available, and you will discover some fascinating facts if you follow astronomers on Twitter.

STARGAZING MEDITATION

Settle down, make yourself warm and comfortable, and try this stargazing meditation:

- Choose a clear night and, if possible, find a place where there is minimal light pollution. If you live in a city, get as high up as you can. The best time to stargaze is during a crescent moon on a crisp winter's night.
- If you need a torch, use one with a red filter, as it won't make it harder for your eyes to focus on the stars in the way that white or blue light will.
- Lie down on the ground, feel the weight of your body and notice how it makes contact with the earth. Appreciate the fact that the ground is supporting you – surrender to that feeling.
- Take three deep breaths.
- Look at one patch of the sky.
- It takes 15 minutes for your eyes to adjust to the dark and the more you look, the more efficient they become.
- Appreciate the vastness of the galaxy beyond. Remind yourself that you are part of it.
- If you get sidetracked by other thoughts, bring your attention gently back to what you are looking at.
- You can close your eyes after a while, if this helps you reach a meditative state.

Here are some of the things you might spot in the night sky:

***Shooting stars** – meteors, which burn up as they pass into the Earth's atmosphere.*

***The International Space Station** – look up when it's next going to be passing through your patch of sky.*

***Star clusters** – groups of stars.*

***Satellites** – there are more than 35,000 satellites orbiting the Earth and several hundred of them can be seen without using a telescope.*

***The moon** – the only celestial body whose surface features can be seen by the unaided eye.*

***The Andromeda Galaxy** – one of the most distant objects that can be viewed with the naked eye.*

***Comets** – balls of ice and rock that develop a trailing tail when getting close to the sun. They are generally difficult to spot, but some are bright enough to be seen with the human eye.*

***Constellations** – patterns of nearby stars.*

PART THREE

RETREAT AWAY

If you want to truly immerse yourself in the retreat experience, there is a plethora of organized events to choose from all over the world. Attending something that has been laid on by somebody else means you can simply show up and dive into the retreat experience without having to worry about any of the planning, or being interrupted by family, friends or deliveries, etc.

You can either choose retreats where you are part of a community and you enjoy your chosen activity with other like-minded individuals or retreats that encourage you to spend time alone.

There are centres in just about every location you can imagine, so consider what type of setting you want before you book. Some of them expect you to share the general chores, others offer unlimited luxury, and the rest cover everything in between.

YOGA

Yoga is an ancient practice, developed in India more than 5,000 years ago, that involves moving your body into a series of postures while controlling your breath and entering a meditative state.

There are several types of yoga, so pick one that's right for you. Some are only suitable for experienced yogis, so if you are a beginner, make sure you are literally not overstretching yourself.

TEN BENEFITS OF YOGA

- Improved flexibility
- A toned body
- More energy
- Reduced stress
- Better breathing patterns
- Mindfulness
- Increased happiness
- A fitter, stronger body
- Nicely stretched muscles
- Relaxation and a sense of inner peace

Most yoga retreats are held in beautiful surroundings and the chances are that you will be asked to hand in or at least switch off your mobile phone. Many places offer additional meditation, breathing and relaxation sessions – check the programme and optional extras before you book. You're likely to return home feeling detoxed, as you'll be moving your body a lot and eating healthy vegetarian or vegan food.

Bring your own yoga mat, strap and blocks if you need them, although many retreats supply the necessary equipment. You will need comfortable, cool clothes that permit ease of movement. A shawl or small blanket is recommended for the relaxation that comes at the end of most yoga sessions. You could also invest in an eye mask – lavender-filled ones are particularly relaxing, as the weight feels comforting on your eyes and they smell wonderful.

TYPES OF YOGA

There are various major branches of yoga, each different in style, and naturally there will be even more variations, depending on the teachers.

Try out several styles before you book an organized yoga retreat – or choose a multi-style retreat if you want to explore the differences while you're away.

Here are some of the most popular forms of yoga you are likely to find on retreat:

Hatha *– one of the most commonly practised forms of yoga, combining gentle movements with breathing. Perfect for beginners.*

Yin *– a slow-paced yoga with seated postures that can be highly meditative. Ideal for beginner yogis.*

Iyengar *– a gentle, precise yoga style that encourages you to move your body into correct alignment and makes use of props. Great for all abilities.*

Vinyasa *– often considered one of the most athletic and creative styles of yoga. The movements are coordinated with the breath and practised in flowing sequences.*

Kundalini *– a very spiritual form of yoga that aims to release your "kundalini", the life-force energy that is said to be trapped in the lower spine.*

Ashtanga *– a dynamic practice that links breath to movements done in quick set sequences with continuous flow. Better suited to experienced yogis.*

Bikram *– an intense practice that involves a series of challenging movements done in a room where the temperature is ramped up. Best for experienced practitioners.*

Power *– a fast-paced practice that improves body strength. Not suitable for beginners.*

Jivamukti *– founded in 1984, this is a vinyasa-flow-style class with Hindu spiritual teaching.*

Aerial yoga *– yoga done while hanging from a low silk hammock that supports your body weight and allows you to do deep stretches and postures in a more relaxed fashion. It's not recommended for absolute beginners.*

MEDITATION

A meditation retreat will give you the opportunity to truly switch off and escape the chaos of everyday life. You will learn the skills to quieten your mind, allowing you to manage stress more effectively. Some say that everything seems so much more vibrant after they've been meditating for a few days – you'll emerge feeling relaxed, well balanced and rejuvenated.

Make sure you know exactly what type of meditation is on offer before you book: you'll find everything from introductory retreats for beginners to more challenging courses, such as vipassana, which can involve sitting still for long stretches and staying silent throughout your stay.

Some meditation retreats are affiliated to religions, while others are secular – whatever type you choose, there is always a spiritual element to the practice and you will probably be encouraged to connect with the life force that runs through everything in the universe.

Try meditating on your own at home or go to some classes at a wellness/ yoga studio before you book a retreat. Read around the subject and see if there are any teachers whose methods you particularly like. There are many different types of meditation offered on retreat and you need to find the one that suits you.

If you are looking for a social break, you are unlikely to find that on a meditation retreat. Much time will be spent in quiet contemplation, and participants are likely to go to bed early and rise at the crack of dawn. You won't be able to watch TV or visit the pub, for example. At the start of the retreat, you will have to make a promise to commit yourself to the process.

TYPES OF MEDITATION

Here are some of the types of meditation you are likely to find on organized retreats:

- **Transcendental meditation** – a silent meditation that involves repeating a silent mantra. It is best done for 20 minutes a day and can only be taught by qualified instructors. It was created by the yogi who instructed The Beatles.
- **Mindfulness meditation** – an effective way to quieten the mind and bring your attention to the present moment. This means letting go of thoughts about the past or future.
- **Vipassana meditation** – an intense practice that involves sitting still for up to ten days, rising at dawn and spending time in silence. The aim is to learn how to control reactions to pain, hunger, boredom, etc.
- **Loving kindness meditation** – this involves focusing on others, and directing positive energy and goodwill towards them. It is often practised at Buddhist retreats.

- **Guided meditation** – great for beginners, as it is teacher-led and following instructions tends to quieten the mind.
- **Self-enquiry meditation** – a process of diving into your psyche and peeling back the layers to explore your beliefs, behaviours and suppressed emotions. Courses usually require you to do some sharing, either with a group or leader.
- **Kundalini meditation** – part of kundalini yoga, this form of meditation aims to awaken and release the kundalini energy that is said to be present at the base of the spine. It is drawn up through the seven "chakras" (energy centres) and released through the crown of the head. This process is said to be good for mental, physical and spiritual health.
- **Zen meditation** – a process of sitting upright and following the breath as it moves in and out of the belly.
- **Chakra meditation** – a technique that is used to keep the body's seven energy centres, known as chakras, in balance.

SILENT

As the name suggests, a silent retreat provides the chance to spend time in quiet contemplation. Some centres enable you to do this alone, while others hold group events run by one or more facilitators.

Spending long periods of time in silence can be hard at first, but if you persevere, the rewards are enormous. Participants often emerge feeling calmer, as well as noticing increased creativity, clarity of mind and a sense of inner peace.

When you aren't speaking and have nothing to distract you, long-buried emotions can sometimes come to the surface, so it is useful to go on a retreat that offers support, should this prove a difficult experience. Many silent retreats for individuals offer one-to-one spiritual coaching sessions as an extra; they also include meditation sessions and offer other gentle activities, such as yoga, Pilates, stretching, and arts and crafts.

During an organized silent retreat, the leaders will speak and participants are sometimes asked to share their experiences of the silence during self-enquiry sessions. If you want to communicate with others outside that time, you'll be allowed to write brief notes or use simple hand gestures.

Most silent retreats take place in beautiful locations, so spending time in nature will be an important part of the experience. If the centre is near shops and cafes, it is best that you avoid them, as spending time there will interfere with the unwinding process.

You can expect to be asked to either hand in or switch off any phones or electronic devices - a few places even ask you to hand over digital watches. There won't be any TV or radio and you're not allowed to read books, newspapers or magazines: the mind slows down during periods of silence, and reading will speed it up again and interrupt the process.

Try to book a day off afterwards or make sure you don't have too many work commitments when you come out of a silent retreat, as you may need to ease yourself gently back into everyday life - it can seem particularly jarring when you've been closeted away for a few days.

SILENT RETREAT ESSENTIALS

Before booking a silent retreat, it is useful to try a short period of silence at home – aiming to manage five hours would be perfect, as it will give you a flavour of what it will be like.

Silent retreats can last from a day to weeks. The longer they are, the harder they can be, but the bigger the rewards. Absolute beginners are advised to start with one day, graduate on to a weekend and then try longer ones.

Before you leave for your retreat, you'll need to tell work colleagues, family and friends that you won't be contactable for a certain period of time. Make sure you clear the decks at home and work, so that you won't be distracted by things you think you should be doing, while you are on retreat.

Here's a list of essentials to consider taking on your silent retreat:

- A non-digital wristwatch
- An alarm clock
- A yoga mat
- A blanket or shawl
- Comfortable clothes
- Luxurious toiletries – for long baths and showers
- A journal
- An eye mask – useful for shutting out the light during yoga or relaxation sessions
- Walking shoes – the chances are that you'll be somewhere remote where there are lots of lovely walks
- A water bottle and snack – for those long walks
- A sketchbook, pencils and paints. Drawing and painting can be very therapeutic when you are on silent retreat
- Contact numbers – give the phone numbers of family members to the centre facilitator, so they can be contacted in the event of an emergency

SPA

Spa retreats generally take place in hotels where there are facilities, such as saunas, steam rooms, hot tubs and a swimming pool, and a number of treatments available. There are sometimes fitness activities and a gym, too.

Organized spa retreats usually include a few classes, use of the facilities, meals and one or two treatments, which you will most likely have to book in advance – do so promptly because some of the most popular ones can get booked up quickly.

Many spa retreats have a theme, so in addition to spending time in the steam room or enjoying a gentle massage, you can opt for other health benefits, such as a cleansing or detoxing diet, or a fitness retreat that will place the emphasis on exercise.

Weekend spa retreats are common, but you can also go for longer and really see the results of your healthier way of living – you will most likely be eating healthy food provided by the venue, doing more exercise than usual and only drinking moderately, if at all.

You can go on a spa retreat alone or with a group of like-minded friends. They are usually not as strict about noise as some other types of retreat, although partying in your room is likely to be frowned upon. You'll be able to relax by the pool and read your favourite magazines or look at your phone.

AMBER
+ MINERAL

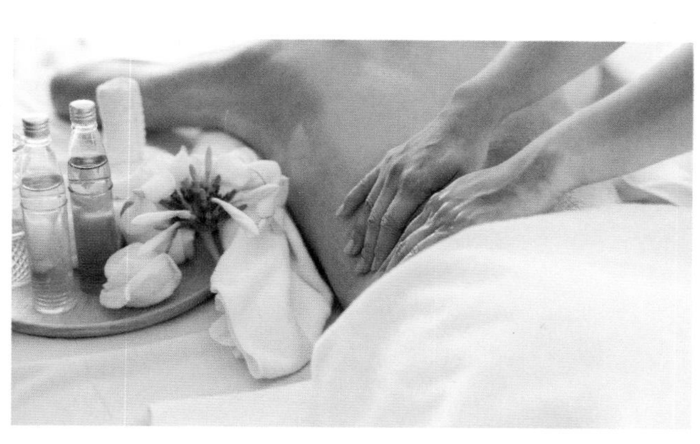

SPA TREATMENTS

Spa resorts nearly always offer a range of relaxing treatments. Here are some of the most popular:

Sauna *– a dry-heat environment that relaxes tired muscles, unclogs pores and can ease itchy skin. Not suitable if you have a heart condition or are pregnant. Listen to your body and don't spend too long in the sauna. Cool down slowly afterwards.*

Hydrotherapy jet *– parts of the body are targeted with short bursts of warm water from a jet to improve circulation and muscle tone.*

Steam room *– a small room heated with steam that helps to ease congestion, soothe sore muscles and loosen joints. Some say it can also boost the immune system. Don't stay in the steam room for more than 20 minutes.*

Seaweed wrap *– pasted on to the skin, this is usually a combination of seawater, clay, essential oils and other ingredients. It is said to remove toxins and tone the skin.*

Tepidarium *– popular in Roman baths, a tepidarium is a small room where heat is constantly radiated from the walls and floor. It is relaxing, soothes sore muscles and is easier to endure than a sauna or steam room, as it is cooler.*

Seaweed bath/mineral soak *– seawater containing minerals, such as iodine, is used in baths or heated wraps, where a paste is applied to the skin and then wrapped in heated towels or a special blanket to treat skin problems, relax muscles and aid circulation.*

WELL-BEING

When it comes to retreats, the term "well-being" covers many different areas, but all of them have one purpose: to ensure that you leave feeling refreshed and renewed.

Whether you are into hiking or Pilates, or just some quiet time followed by an aromatherapy massage, you'll find well-being retreats across the world, and often in the most stunning locations.

While some establishments run group activities, there are many that offer a tailor-made experience for individuals, although bespoke programmes can be expensive.

Being on a well-being retreat doesn't mean you necessarily have to abstain from alcohol or avoid meat, as many resorts offer breaks that include cocktails by the pool with a full menu of à la carte dishes.

Here are some of the activities you are likely to find on a well-being retreat:

- **Pilates** – a low-impact exercise consisting of movement that builds strength and endurance.
- **Yoga** – a series of poses that are combined with breath work and meditation.
- **Zumba** – an exercise class that combines Latin beats with aerobics.
- **TRX** – total body resistance exercise, invented by a Navy SEAL, which uses body weight to increase strength.
- **Guided imagery relaxation** – a guide talks you through a relaxing meditation by suggesting pleasing images.
- **Juicing** – consuming drinks that are made from a combination of fruits and vegetables.
- **Detoxing** – eating a diet that is mainly plant-based, with no processed foods or alcohol. The aim is to rid your body of toxins.
- **Meditation and mindfulness** – classes, work-shops and instructions on how to meditate and be mindful are often an integral part of well-being retreats.
- **Massage** – frequently available as an extra at spa retreats and well-being centres. There are many different options, such as deep tissue massage, shiatsu (where the therapist uses their hands and palms to work the whole body) and Thai massage (which involves your body being stretched and twisted in various positions).

HOLISTIC THERAPIES

Here's a selection of some of the holistic therapies that are offered by many retreat centres:

- Reflexology – a deeply relaxing treatment where different parts of the feet, lower legs, hands, face and ears are massaged. It is based on the idea that these correspond to different areas of the body, and that applying pressure and massaging them can promote healing and restore balance. For example, the big toe is thought to be linked to the head, while the heel of the foot relates to the buttocks.
- Ayurveda – a healing system developed in ancient India and based on the belief that wellness depends on a balance between mind, body and spirit. A treatment plan may include massage, oils, herbs, enemas, and a diet tailored to suit your personality and body type.
- Acupuncture – thin needles are lightly inserted into the skin to correct energy imbalances in the body.
- Aromatherapy massage – a soothing massage done with base oils that contain the concentrated oils of various plants. Each essential oil has certain properties and the therapist will blend a mix that suits your requirements.

- Craniosacral therapy – a gentle form of bodywork that uses light pressure on the head, neck and back to relieve stress and pain.
- Reiki – a Japanese practice that works to heal energy blockages in the body to restore it to health. A therapist will either touch your fully-clothed body lightly or hold their hands just above it.
- Hot stone therapy – a relaxing massage that is done through touch and the laying of flat hot stones along the spine. The hot stones warm the muscles and therefore deeper pressure can be applied during the massage.

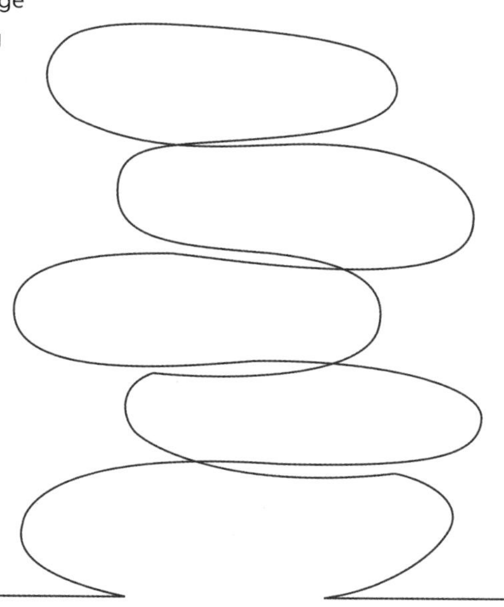

MINDFULNESS

Mindfulness is a term used to describe a state in which the mind is focused on only one thing: the present moment. It sounds simple enough and while we're all born with the ability to be mindful, it's a skill we generally lose during adulthood, when it can be hard to escape the clutches of a busy mind.

Mindfulness retreats aim to help you calm the mind and appreciate the wonder of the present moment. You'll learn how to deal with difficult emotions, negative thoughts and your "inner critic" – and these will be skills you can use to be mindful in everyday life.

They do this with a combination of instruction, meditation, periods of silence and relaxation sessions. Some offer yoga and other meditative activities. Most mindfulness retreats are off the beaten track, and hiking and getting close to nature are encouraged.

You should walk away from a mindfulness retreat with a sense of inner peace and the tools that will enable you to navigate daily life with a sense of ease, joy and calm.

If you are not already convinced, here are ten reasons to be mindful:

- Mindfulness helps to dampen down the body's "flight" response, which is designed to keep you out of harm's way. You will learn to recognize when fight-and-flight emotions flood your body, and it will get easier to step back rather than respond automatically. This, in turn, will decrease stress and anxiety.
- It helps to reduce the grip of addictions and compulsive behaviour, by enabling you to recognize your impulses, observe them and choose not to react.
- When practised during exercise, it makes the workout more effective because you can focus on the movement rather than be carried away by thoughts.
- You'll be able to concentrate better.
- It will get your creative juices flowing.
- It can improve your relationships with others by helping you to understand yourself and the trigger points that can lead to disagreements.
- Your energy levels are likely to increase.
- You'll feel more confident.
- It will be easier to love yourself.
- It can prevent overeating.

CRAFTING

You don't have to be particularly creative to enjoy the benefits of a crafting retreat. Most of us are born with a love of making and doing, and that's a part of ourselves that can be reawakened there.

There are hundreds of crafting retreats to choose from. You could try:

- Quilting
- Boro mending – a Japanese technique where fabrics are stitched together to mend holes or tears
- Art
- Jewellery making
- Scrapbooking
- Knitting or crocheting
- Sewing
- Collage
- Découpage – gluing paper cut-outs on to a picture to create a 3D effect and using paint to enhance it

Whatever craft you pick, remember that making something is a chance to express yourself. Every person on the retreat will create something totally unique and your work will communicate more about you than you could imagine.

You'll be encouraged to use your hands rather than your head – this can prove highly meditative and the time will whizz by. Crafting keeps your mind sharp, plus it's relaxing, challenging and mood-boosting. It's also a great way to socialize without the pressure of having to think of too many topics of conversation.

BORO-MENDING TECHNIQUE

If you want to sample some crafting at home, try this simple Boro-mending technique.

You will need

Scissors
Fabric for patching (cotton is best)
Jeans with a hole to repair
Pins
Ruler
Chalk
Embroidery thread
Chenille needles (embroidery needles with a long eye and sharp tip)

Method

- Cut a square or rectangle of fabric slightly larger than the hole you are mending.
- Turn the jeans inside out and pin the patch in place over the hole.
- Turn the jeans right side out and, with a ruler and the chalk, draw a series of parallel horizontal lines across the ripped area, about 4 mm apart.
- Turn the jeans inside out again and stitch through the denim at the bottom edge of your guiding lines, ensuring you sew through the denim and the patch.
- Next, turn the jeans right side out again and do a running stitch (a basic straight stitch done by passing the needle in and out of the fabric at a regular distance) along the first line. Try to make the stitches as small and even as possible.
- When you have completed a single line, pull the thread to ensure the tension is even on the front and back.
- Once the first row is finished, start on the second. When you have completed all the lines in one colour, secure your thread with a discreet knot and cut.
- Add more decorative stitching, if you wish. You could do a running stitch in between the lines you've just done with a different colour, decorate with some cross-stitches or try vertical lines. Experiment!
- When you've finished, turn the jeans inside out and trim off any excess material around the patch.

WRITING

You don't have to be the next Shakespeare to enjoy and benefit from a writing retreat, as they are pitched at all levels of ability, from absolute beginners through to those who are polishing off a novel, film script or play.

A love of writing is essential, but that's all you need – along with a laptop or a notebook and pen, if you prefer.

Writing retreats can be found all over the world in every kind of location you can imagine, such as the side of a mountain, a city or a coastal town. Most are organized by writers who will empathize if you lack confidence or can't stop procrastinating. Lots of writing retreats also hire well-known authors as tutors, and their experience and guidance can prove invaluable.

A good place to start is to decide what kind of writing retreat you'd enjoy most. Here are a few examples of the things on offer:

- Memoir writing
- Short-story writing
- Non-fiction courses
- Novels
- Playwriting
- Film scripts
- TV scripts
- Radio plays
- Poetry
- Children's and young adult fiction
- No classes - just a quiet space for you to concentrate on your writing project

WHAT HAPPENS ON A WRITING RETREAT?

Most writing retreats are residential and include meals. Some expect you to pitch in with the washing-up, while others cater for you - check what's available before you book.

The secret to getting the best experience is to listen to the tutor's advice, enjoy the process of writing and be kind to yourself - all writers complete many drafts of a work before it's published, so don't be upset if you don't like the first thing you come up with - it's a normal part of the writing process. Ernest Hemingway wrote 47 endings to his book *A Farewell to Arms*, so you are in great company if you dislike your first draft!

Writing is a wonderful activity to lose yourself in and you'll need to relax, because all your best ideas will come from your unconscious mind - that's the mysterious bit of you that is outside of your conscious awareness. Taking a break from your writing, going for a walk, relaxing, and so on are all great ways to allow the unconscious mind to get to work and breathe life into your prose.

A writing retreat is more than just a place to write. You will learn a lot about the process of crafting a novel, screenplay or whatever it is you want to create. You'll get supportive and honest feedback, plus your creative streak will be given free rein - and that in itself is an intensely rewarding experience.

READING

Who doesn't like curling up with a fantastic book – and plenty of spare hours to read all the way to the end? Reading on retreat is a wonderful way to escape a busy life, immerse yourself in another world and enjoy some other relaxing activities on the side, such walking, meditation and journaling.

You can either book yourself into a retreat centre that caters for individuals and take your own books or sign up specifically for a reading retreat. They generally take place in lovely locations in the countryside or by the sea and offer lots of time to read without distraction, away from ringing phones, to-do lists and commitments. It's the perfect way to read guilt-free and something you can do year-round. In the summer months, you can settle in the shade to read outdoors, whereas in winter, you can wrap yourself in blankets and bask in the glow of a real fire.

You can, of course, take your own selection of books, but many places offer a range of reading material that has been vetted and is considered perfect for retreaters, with something to suit all tastes. Many reading retreats also invite guest authors to come and talk about their writing and the books that have influenced them.

Reading retreats are generally fully catered and you can either eat on your own or enjoy the company of other book lovers.

If you are considering a reading retreat, here are nine thought-provoking and uplifting reads:

- *Big Magic* by Elizabeth Gilbert - a thoughtful and inspiring non-fiction book on the pursuit of joy and creativity.
- *An American Marriage* by Tayari Jones - a touching love story offering an intimate look into the hearts and minds of the three main characters.
- *Homegoing* by Yaa Gyasi - a tale of two separated sisters, born in eighteenth-century Ghana; spanning three continents and several generations, this book tells the story of their lives and legacies.
- *Little Women* by Louisa May Alcott - a classic coming-of-age book about four sisters growing up in Massachusetts during the nineteenth century.
- *The Unlikely Pilgrimage of Harold Fry* by Rachel Joyce - a retiree's unexpected tale of adventure, reminiscence and reconciliation as he travels on foot across the English countryside.
- *White Teeth* by Zadie Smith - an epic, humorous and celebrated book following the fortune of two families from Jamaica and Bangladesh.
- *Around the World in 80 Days* by Jules Verne - the story of a Victorian gentleman, Phileas Fogg, and his hair-raising adventures around the world.
- *The Happiness Project* by Gretchen Rubin - one person's year-long attempt to uncover true joy and contentment.
- *Where the Crawdads Sing* by Delia Owens - a poignant tale of loneliness, survival and love set in twentieth-century North Carolina.

WALKING

If exploring new places on foot is your thing, then a walking retreat will offer a relaxing, adventurous break that will leave you feeling fit and energized. Walking retreats are generally located in fantastic settings, where the leaders know all the best trails.

Some centres make walking a focal point of the programme, while others offer it alongside a variety of activities, such as yoga and possibly even a range of spa treatments. Some also offer mindfulness training as part of the break, and this can include walking meditation and mindful walking.

You can be as adventurous as you like with a walking retreat. You could opt for a bracing coastal hike or travel to a destination where you trek along paths used by bears and wolves in breathtaking forests. You'll find walking retreats organized all across the world, from the foothills of the Himalayas through to Greek islands and country manors.

The majority of walking retreats offer accommodation and food, and you'll most likely have a guide for the trails, although some centres do encourage walkers to explore alone, with the help of a map – always carry a whistle, though, in case you get lost.

Before you book a walking retreat, check what level of fitness is required for the treks, because some will be more demanding than others. The walks generally last between two and four hours, but some can take longer.

Walking retreats are a fantastic way to meet like-minded people of all ages and from all backgrounds, while being outdoors and surrounded by stunning scenery.

Here's a list of some of the items you'll need to pack for a walking retreat:

- Waterproof jacket and trousers
- Walking trousers
- Long- and short-sleeved tops
- Hiking socks
- Walking boots
- A hat
- Sunscreen
- Plasters
- Mosquito repellent
- Painkillers
- Blister treatment – just in case
- Lip balm
- A small rucksack
- A water bottle

NORDIC WALKING

There is also the option of a Nordic walking retreat. This is a form of walking that utilizes poles to enhance the experience. It was developed in Finland, where cross-country skiers started using their sticks when there was no snow and realized that it did wonders for their fitness.

With Nordic walking, you move your upper body in a similar way to cross-country skiers: the poles help to propel you along, which makes you work harder because it feels as if there is less strain on the legs. Studies say that it burns up to 46 per cent more calories than normal walking, since the upper body is used, and it reduces the impact on joints.

It is a specific fitness technique not to be confused with trekking, hill walking or trail running, as the poles actively encourage the use of the upper body. It is not something you can go off and do on your own, without instruction, as it is imperative that you get the technique right. Nordic walking is only taught by qualified instructors and is popular in Europe.

Be warned: Nordic walkers tend to like a challenge, so the route is likely to be hilly in parts. There are a range of levels, so make sure that your chosen retreat will suit your ability. The correct poles with a hand strap are essential, as are comfortable walking shoes.

TEN BENEFITS OF NORDIC WALKING

- Can be done anywhere
- Easy to learn
- You can talk as you go
- Encourages you to exercise in nature
- Tones upper and lower body
- Uses 90 per cent of the skeletal muscles
- Reduces pressure on knees and joints
- Good for neck, back and shoulder problems
- Provides cardiovascular benefits
- Benefits the immune system by boosting the lymphatic system

COOKERY

There is a cookery retreat to suit every taste and whatever type you choose, you'll return home with new lifelong skills. When you invest in yourself, it's never a waste of money!

Cookery retreats that look at nutrition and show you how to cook healthy meals are very popular. They will not only teach you the fundamentals of good health, but you'll also learn how your body reacts to certain foods and what you should eat to maintain optimum health. A vast majority of the cookery retreats that look at health and nutrition will offer sessions in other holistic practices, such as meditation, yoga and Pilates.

Of course, if you'd rather spend a weekend baking, then there are retreats for that too, with masterclasses in everything from artisan bread to the perfect puff pastry.

Cookery retreats are held in all kinds of locations, so you may need to think about what you'd like to do when you're not in the kitchen. Choose a seaside spot and you'll get to walk on the beach in the evenings or, if you like a bit of hustle and bustle, something based in a town might be more fun.

When you sign up to a cookery retreat, there is no spectating – there'll be plenty of support if you need it, but you'll be expected to prepare food. A chef will demonstrate, and those on the course will have their own station and oven where they prepare the dishes.

TYPES OF COOKERY RETREAT

- Bake from scratch
- Artisan baking
- Balinese flavours
- Raw food
- Italian cuisine
- Patisserie
- Vegan
- Low sugar
- Cakes
- Macaroons
- Fresh pasta
- Viennoiserie

If you are really serious about cooking, there are lots of retreats run by celebrity chefs. They can be costly, but if your dish doesn't work then the great thing is that you get to taste something made by your favourite chef.

SOURDOUGH RECIPES

There has been a boom in popularity for sourdough starter bread, which is a loaf that is made using a live culture of flour and water instead of yeast. It's easy to do: all you need is some strong white flour and plenty of patience. The great thing about a sourdough starter is that it never stops growing. Every time you use a bit, some more will grow. You'll be amazed at the naturally leavened bread you can make with such ease.

SOURDOUGH STARTER RECIPE

You will need

50 g white bread flour
50 g tepid water
A 750 ml glass jar with a lid
More flour and water to top up your starter, as necessary

Method

- To make your starter, mix 50 g flour with 50 g tepid water. Place this in a jar, replace the lid and leave at room temperature for 24 hours.
- On day two, repeat this process and add the new mixture to yesterday's batch.
- Do this every day for five days.
- By the fifth day, it should be bubbling and it will smell like yogurt – if that's the case, then it's ready and you can now make your bread!
- Each time you use it, pour half of the starter into a separate container and then feed the remaining mixture with 100 g flour and 100 g water, and leave at room temperature.

SOURDOUGH BREAD RECIPE

Makes: 2 loaves

Ingredients

1 tbsp sourdough starter
600 g tepid water
1 kg white bread flour
20 g sea salt
Cold water

Method

- Mix 1 tbsp of starter with 600 g tepid water and stir.
- Tip this mixture into the flour and make a rough dough with a spatula.
- When the flour is mixed in, cover and leave to prove (rise) somewhere warm for up to four hours.
- Sprinkle salt on the dough, add another 50 g of water and mix into the dough.
- Take the dough and stretch it over itself a few times.
- Cover and leave for 30 minutes.
- Repeat this process twice more and leave the dough for a further three hours.
- Split the dough in two, fold each piece into itself to form a ball and leave uncovered for 30 minutes.
- Cover the dough and chill overnight.
- Preheat the oven to 230°C/450°F. Place cold water in a baking tray on the lowest shelf of the oven to create steam. Score the loaves and bake for 34–40 minutes, until a good crust has formed. Store them in a bread bin and eat within five days.

FITNESS

Choose a fitness retreat and you know you are going to sweat a lot, wonder why you signed up for something so physical and then return home feeling fantastic.

Fitness retreats come in all shapes and sizes, and choosing one boils down to personal taste. Many take place in scenic locations, so you can expect to be exercising outdoors. They also tend to utilize their environments – if you are on the coast, you will be offered certain activities, like barefoot beach circuits, or if there are miles of smooth country roads, cycling might be on the agenda.

The important thing is to do your research. Consider your level of fitness, the type of exercise you enjoy and what kind of surroundings will inspire you.

Some fitness retreats offer a weight-loss element and will provide personal trainers, yoga teachers, life coaches, nutritionists and chefs. Many can boast facilities such as a spa, swimming pool, tennis courts and a gym.

A good fitness retreat will offer a balanced approach and you shouldn't feel the need to overdo it or return home with aching muscles. There'll be appropriate advice on how to stretch before and after exercise, and fitness sessions will be followed by wind-down activities such as yoga, a spa treatment or sports massage.

The majority of retreats offer accommodation, as well as a selection of light and nutritious meals. If you are short on time, there are some day-long fitness retreats on offer that aim to prepare you for a fitter way of life. Some even include email aftercare support in the package, so that you can keep up the good habits you've learned.

TYPES OF FITNESS RETREAT

Cycling – a great activity for all levels of ability that is easy on the joints. Make sure you wear a helmet and padded cycle shorts. A removable gel seat cover will also make the rides more comfortable.

Wild swimming – this is a term used to describe swimming in any natural body of water, such as the sea, a river or a lake. It will feel much colder than a swimming pool, so wearing a wetsuit is advisable. You should never go wild swimming alone and if there are boats on the water, make sure you use a safety buoy to signal your presence.

Trail running – running uphill and over uneven surfaces is great fun, and you'll get to see some awesome scenery, but it's not suitable for those who are new to running.

Circuit training – a series of exercises that are repeated a certain number of times before you move on to the next. They are designed to work out all major muscle groups.

Altitude training – the process of exercising anywhere that is more than 2,400 m above sea level. It prepares athletes to cope with endurance and is not suitable for beginners.

HIIT – this stands for high-intensity interval training and involves doing short intense periods of exercise until you are too exhausted to continue.

Assault course – an individual or a team completes a series of challenging obstacles that require a mix of climbing, crawling, running, jumping and balancing. It's a fun activity for all ages, but make sure you do a course that is suitable for your abilities.

SPIRITUAL

Any retreat that offers holistic therapies plus meditation and mindfulness experiences will have a spiritual element, but that doesn't mean you have to believe in anything in particular. It is an intensely personal matter and all you need to benefit is an open mind.

To be spiritual means you appreciate that we are all connected to something bigger than ourselves. Some people call this God, while to others it is simply the energy that runs through all living things or an unknowable intelligence that created the universe.

Spirituality does incorporate elements of religion, but nowadays it is a much broader concept. In your search for a spiritual retreat, you will find many that are run by organized religions and others that are not. It all comes down to personal preference.

When you go on a spiritual retreat, you will be offered the opportunity to feel a meaningful connection with the invisible energy that is bigger than yourself. There are many paths to this and everybody's journey is different, but here are some of the activities that have helped people to find enlightenment:

- Yoga
- Silence
- Meditation
- Mindfulness
- Dance (such as 5Rhythms, a movement meditation practice)
- Tai chi
- Reiki
- Healing
- Detox

Most spiritual retreats recognize that people have different beliefs and expectations, and that you can be a spiritual person without having any affiliation to a certain religion. They will welcome you with open arms, whatever your background. Don't worry too much if there are elements of the spiritual teachings you don't agree with: discard anything that doesn't resonate and learn from any bits that do.

Whatever kind of spiritual retreat you go on, you'll need to accept that a large portion of the time will be spent in quiet contemplation, because ultimately nobody can enlighten you - it has to come from within.

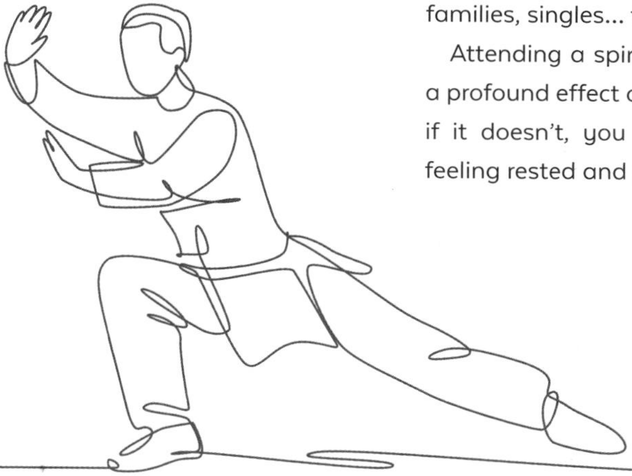

Pack a journal to jot down your thoughts and feelings throughout the retreat and, as the majority of spiritual retreats are set in stunning locations, take the time to explore and get close to nature.

Accommodation is likely to be provided, and you might benefit from a generous discount if you are prepared to share. The food at spiritual retreats is very often vegetarian and vegan, with gluten- and dairy-free options readily available.

Spiritual retreats are so popular, it is possible to find one that feels tailor-made for you: some are set up for individuals, while others are designed for groups; there are all-women or all-men retreats, as well as those for parents, families, singles... the choice is endless.

Attending a spiritual retreat can have a profound effect on your life - and even if it doesn't, you are likely to emerge feeling rested and peaceful.

RELIGIOUS

You don't have to be a believer to benefit from a religious retreat and many openly advertise this. What you'll find will undoubtedly be a peaceful place where you can take time out to relax, reflect and connect with the divine. Believing in a god or going to church are not prerequisites – all that any centre asks is that you are respectful of their religion. Here are some examples of retreats that welcome people of all denominations and are not heavily based on theological practice or learning:

- Christian retreats – these offer a quiet space, time for reflection and an opportunity to deepen your spiritual life. Non-Christians and beginners are usually welcome, with retreats running from six hours up to 30 days, depending on the programme.
- Buddhist retreats – Buddhists spend their time trying to cultivate wisdom, kindness and compassion through the practice of meditation. There are many different schools of Buddhism, so you will need to do some research to find the best fit for you. Consider the location and activities on offer, and find out if you are expected to pitch in with chores. Buddhist retreats are perfect for beginners, as some short meditation sessions lasting just 15 minutes and guided walking meditations are likely to be part of the timetable. Many Buddhist centres ask for a donation rather than charging a set fee for retreats.
- Quaker retreats – many Quaker centres offer self-catering stays that give you time for reflection, relaxation and periods of silence. You will most likely be invited to join the Quakers for their daily worship, but this is generally not

obligatory. They are a Christian denomination and the emphasis is on your personal journey along the spiritual path. Writing, study, painting, journaling, etc. are actively encouraged.

- Taoist retreats – these follow the Taoist tradition and combine spiritual pursuits, such as meditation and mindfulness, with sessions that promote health and vitality, such as qigong, tai chi, dao-yin self-massage, energy work and holistic medicine. The aim is to allow the life force that moves through the body to flow freely. The retreats are suitable for all ages and some offer extra activities, such as a sweat lodge, which is a traditional ceremony involving purification of the body with steam – a bit like a large sauna.
- Shamanic retreats – shamanism is a religious practice that encourages followers to connect to the spiritual world through a state of altered consciousness. There was a time when it was associated with tribes, but shamanism now has a growing following all over the world. Shamanic retreats are nearly always set in rural locations, as connecting with nature is an important element. There is a central belief that everybody has an inner shaman who knows the answers to all of life's problems – and you will be taught how to access it.

There are many other religious retreats available, including Jewish, Muslim, Sikh and Hindu retreats. Before booking, it is always best to check if they are geared towards those who share the faith or are open to all comers.

VOICE WORK

You don't have to be a fantastic singer to benefit enormously from a retreat that encourages the use of your vocal cords in all manner of different ways, from singing and chanting through to speaking out and expressing yourself.

The voice is an important tool: people make judgements about others based on how they sound; it enables us to connect and gives us the ability to express ourselves personally. It is also a tool that can be used therapeutically.

Studies show that singing can boost the immune system, and learning to use the voice effectively can improve mental health, lift the mood and aid relaxation.

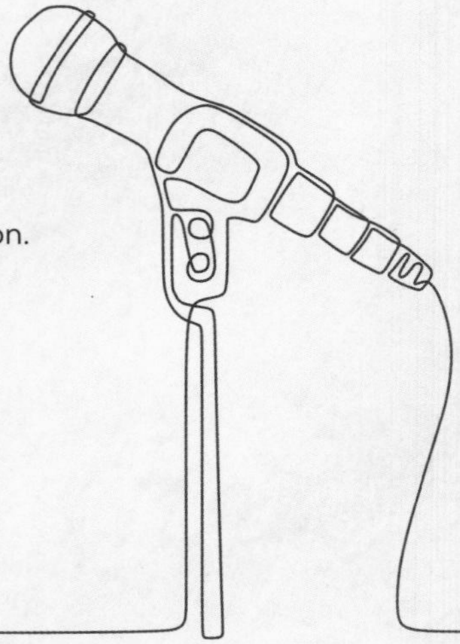

Here are several of the common voice-work retreats on offer:

Sacred singing *– musical mantras, sacred chants and prayers set to music are said to aid healing, peace and a connection to the universal life force.*

Kirtan *– the singing and chanting of sacred mantras in ancient languages; said to cleanse the heart and mind.*

Mongolian overtone singing *– this is a form of chanting traditionally found in Central Asia that produces high flute-like tones when done by a group of people and is undertaken as a spiritual, meditative and healing practice.*

Chanting *– the repetition of words and phrases to induce a meditative state. It is said to promote healing and boost your mood.*

Holistic voice therapy *– the use of voice, breathing and vocal exercises to heal and boost emotional, physical and spiritual health.*

Freeing your voice *– learning to relax, breathe, open your throat and articulate your voice.*

Singing *– vocal workshops and singing with a group in various styles on retreat are often combined with other activities, such as yoga or tai chi.*

Voice arts therapy *– a method of exploring the voice, as well as enabling better communication and self-expression.*

SOUND

Sound has been used to cure numerous ailments for thousands of years and is currently a popular healing tool on retreat. Sound healing can happen in a number of ways, from playing selected pieces of music to the use of various instruments.

We perceive sound in the form of waves and once the brain has processed them, they trigger responses in our bodies. Studies show that listening to music can relieve stress, enhance creativity and boost the mood. When we hear a pleasant noise or piece of music, the brain releases natural painkilling hormones into the bloodstream.

Generally, people who go on sound retreats find them intensely relaxing and all that's needed is a willingness to surrender to the vibrations.

Here are some of the practices you might find on offer at sound-healing retreats:

- Binaural beats – different tones are played into each ear via headphones. They synchronize in the brain and trigger a healing response.
- Bonny Method – a style of music therapy that uses music, alongside guided imagery, to heal patients.
- Gong bathing – participants lie down and immerse themselves in the sound of gongs. This is often followed by the playing of wind chimes, which encourages feelings of joy and relaxation. Let the facilitator know in advance if you have sensitive ears, as the gongs can be very loud. The experience is said to boost wellness and induce a meditative state.
- Singing bowl therapy – gong- and bell-like sounds are produced by a series of metallic bowls that have been used since the twelfth century for meditation purposes. The experience is incredibly soothing.
- Tuning-fork therapy – tuning forks are applied to specific parts of the body in the belief that the vibrations they create will restore emotional balance.

PERSONAL DEVELOPMENT

Personal development retreats offer you the opportunity to delve into your psyche, get to know yourself a bit better and learn how to change your behaviour, in order to live the life you crave.

It is not for the faint-hearted, as you'll be encouraged to examine feelings that may have been buried for years, as well as taking a long, hard look at limiting beliefs and being honest about any patterns of behaviour that are holding you back.

Because it can be an intense process, you should think carefully about which personal development retreat you choose. Do your research on the facilitators; find out what qualifications and experience they have, and read as many client testimonials as you can. Wherever possible, try to do a one-to-one session with the therapist – you should be able to do this online. It's important that you feel comfortable with the people who are leading you on this delicate journey.

Most personal development retreats are run for groups and you will be asked to share your experiences with others. It is a confidential space and participants will be told that whatever they hear on retreat stays on retreat.

Holistic practices – such as meditation and mindfulness – are often offered as well. Before booking, check what is on the schedule to ensure that it is all to your liking.

Everybody is different and it is hard to predict what you will get from a personal development retreat, but you should emerge with deeper self-knowledge, a greater willingness to face your fears and a liberating sense that you are in the driving seat when it comes to your own destiny.

Once you've been on a personal development retreat, you embark on a journey that doesn't end, as you will continue to learn more about yourself as time goes on. You may wish to go on subsequent retreats that offer the opportunity to get to know yourself on an even more profound level.

TYPES OF PERSONAL DEVELOPMENT RETREAT

- Heal your inner child: we were all kids once and there are many workshops which will help you to address patterns of behaviour that were laid down when you were very young and might still be holding you back as an adult.
- Feminine wisdom: all-female retreats that encourage the exploration of feminine power and wisdom.
- Men's retreats: men also get an opportunity to explore their emotions in the company of other men.
- Love with courage/Path of Love: courses that encourage you to let go of past trauma, open your heart and accept love – both from others and from yourself.
- The Pattern System: a system that encourages you to explore your psyche to find your strengths and weaknesses.
- Wealth mastery: retreats that instruct you on how to bring abundance and more money into your life.
- Unleash your power: find inner peace, believe in yourself and discover an inner strength you didn't know you had.
- Couples therapy: retreats aimed at helping couples strengthen their intimacy, communicate better and even improve their sex lives.
- Equine therapy: also known as hippotherapy (from the Greek word *hippos*, which means "horse"), this pairs people with horses in order to induce calm, relaxation and overall well-being through riding.

CONCLUSION

Traditionally, retreats were extremely serious spiritual affairs that required long periods of silence and contemplation, but they've changed a lot in the modern day. There are now plenty of organized retreats to choose from that are like a holiday, where somebody else has planned the itinerary and is preparing all your meals. It's a break from your everyday life in the truest sense of the word: you don't need to think about anything other than relaxing and immersing yourself in hand-picked experiences.

There's no pressure to go anywhere or do any particular activities when it comes to your own personal retreat time – it's all about what *you* want and giving yourself the ideal opportunity to *be* rather than *do*.

The chances are that you'll unwind, sleep better than ever and come out of your retreat experience feeling invigorated, whether you choose to do it at home or at a different venue. What are you waiting for? The bliss of retreat is there for you to dive into whenever you choose. Enjoy!

IMAGE CREDITS

Front cover photo by Anton Sharov on Unsplash; back cover top photo © Anna Ok/Shutterstock.com; back cover middle photo by Jen P on Unsplash; back cover bottom photo © Daria Minaeva/Shutterstock.com; pp.4–5 © Irtsya/Shutterstock.com; pp.4–5, 18, 24, 34, 46, 50, 72, 86, 90, 100, 106, 110, 118, 122, 128, 144, 148, 158–159 © VolodymyrSanych/Shutterstock.com; pp.6–7 © SEE D JAN/Shutterstock.com; p.8 © Marina Suslova/Shutterstock.com; p.10 photo by Noemi Jimenez on Unsplash; p.11 photo by Jen P on Unsplash; p.13 top left photo by Kari Shea on Unsplash; p.13 top right photo by Minh Pham on Unsplash; p.13 bottom left photo by Element 5 on Unsplash; p.13 bottom right photo by Logan Nolin on Unsplash; p.14 © Anna Ok/Shutterstock.com; pp.16–17 © Gita Kulinitch Studio/Shutterstock.com; p.19 © Burunduk's/Shutterstock.com; p.20 © nampix/Shutterstock.com; p.21 © FotoHelin/Shutterstock.com; p.22 © FotoHelin/Shutterstock.com; p.23 © Alena Ozerova/Shutterstock.com; p.25 © Derplan13/Shutterstock.com; p.27 © Mny-Jhee/Shutterstock.com; p.29 © Africa Studio/Shutterstock.com; pp.30–31 © Natasha Breen/Shutterstock.com; p.32 top left photo by Georgia de Lotz on Unsplash; p.32 top right photo by Jean Philippe Delberghe on Unsplash; p.32 bottom left photo by Fotografierende on Unsplash; p.32 bottom right corner photo by Glen Carrie on Unsplash; p.34 © NikVector/Shutterstock.com; pp.36–37 © Daria Minaeva/Shutterstock.com; p.38 photo by Felicity Mikellides on Unsplash; p.39 photo by Jason Leung on Unsplash; p.41 photo by Sincerely Media on Unsplash; pp.42–43 © 279photo Studio/Shutterstock.com; p.44 © Maria Kovalets/Shutterstock.com; p.47 © one line man/Shutterstock.com; p.49 © Valentina_G/Shutterstock.com; p.51 © NikVector/Shutterstock.com; pp.52–53 © Aleksey Mnogosmyslov/Shutterstock.com; p.55 photo by Larisa Birta on Unsplash; p.56 © Oxana Denezhkina/Shutterstock.com; p.57 © Oleksandra Naumenko/Shutterstock.com; p.58 © Ekaterina Kondratova/Shutterstock.com; pp.60–61© Artamonova Alla/Shutterstock.com; p.62 photo by Erda Estremera on Unsplash; p.65 photo by Aaron Burden on Unsplash; pp.66–67 © Zoia Kostina/Shutterstock.com; p.68 top left photo © Silkspin/Shutterstock.com; p.68 top right photo © vaivirga/Shutterstock.com; p.68 middle right photo © Inna Skaldutska/Shutterstock.com; p.68 bottom left photo © BBA Photography/Shutterstock.com; p.68 bottom right photo © Shebeko/Shutterstock.com; p.71 top left photo © Gunter Kremer/Shutterstock.com; p.71 top right photo © photopia/Shutterstock.com; p.71 middle left photo © Moomusician/Shutterstock.com; p.71 middle photo © AVN

Photo Lab/Shutterstock.com; p.71 bottom left photo © carekung/Shutterstock.com; p.71 bottom middle photo © stefbennett/ Shutterstock.com; p.71 bottom right photo © Maren Winter/Shutterstock.com; p.72 © Ikidogoooo/Shutterstock.com; p.74 © elena moiseeva/Shutterstock.com; p.75 © Peter Fuzia/Shutterstock.com; p.76–77 © KreaFoto/Shutterstock.com; p.78 photo by Insung Yoon on Unsplash; p.79 photo by Peng Chen on Unsplash; p.80 photo by Hunt Han on Unsplash; p.82 © Olha Rohulya/Shutterstock.com; p.85 © NoirChocolate/Shutterstock.com; p.86 © Valenty/Shutterstock.com; p.88 © Vitalii Nesterchuk/Shutterstock.com; p.89 © Ahmed Zayan/Shutterstock.com; p.90 © DODOMO/Shutterstock.com; pp.92–93 © EMRstock/Shutterstock.com; p.94 photo by Hermansyah on Unsplash; p.96 © Alexey Fedorenko/Shutterstock.com; p.97 © Kharlanov Evgeny/Shutterstock.com; pp.98–99 photo by Felix Mittermeier on Unsplash; p.100 © Singleline/Shutterstock.com; p.102 © Alena Ozerova/Shutterstock.com; p.104 photo by Erik Brolin on Unsplash; p.105 © Magdanatka/Shutterstock.com; p.106 © Valenty/Shutterstock.com; p.108 © fizkes/Shutterstock.com; p.111 © one line man/Shutterstock.com; p.112 © ivan_kislitsin/Shutterstock.com; p.113 © zjuzjaka/Shutterstock.com; pp.114–115 © Pixel-Shot/Shutterstock.com; p.117 top left photo by Ellie Elien on Unsplash; p.117 top right photo © worawit_j/Shutterstock.com; p.117 bottom left photo by Maja Petric on Unsplash; p.117 middle right photo © Alena Ozerova/Shutterstock.com; p.117 bottom right photo © Still AB/Shutterstock.com; p.118 © Valenty/Shutterstock.com; p.120 photo by Mae Mo on Unsplash; p.123 © one line man/Shutterstock.com; p.124 © Yevhenii Chulovskyi/Shutterstock.com; p.125 photo by Chelsea Gates on Unsplash; pp.126–127 © White bear studio/Shutterstock.com; p.128 © one line man/Shutterstock.com; p.130 photo by Taisiia Shestopal on Unsplash; p.131 © Egasit Mullakhut/Shutterstock.com; p.133 © Izf/Shutterstock.com; p.134 © Zoom Team /Shutterstock.com; p.137 © stockcreations/Shutterstock.com; p.138 © Zagorulko Inka/Shutterstock.com; p.139 © Dariia Belkina/Shutterstock.com; p.140 © Dirima/Shutterstock.com; p.142 top left photo © mimagephotography/ Shutterstock.com; p.142 top right photo © Dea e Bruno/Shutterstock.com; p.142 middle left photo © Jacob Lund/Shutterstock.com; p.142 middle photo © AboutLife/ Shutterstock.com; p.142 bottom left photo © bodiaphvideo/Shutterstock.com; p.142 bottom right photo © Maridav/Shutterstock.com; p.142 bottom middle photo by Emilio Garcia on Unsplash; p.145 © Simple Line/ Shutterstock.com; p.146 photo by Gabriel Testoni on Unsplash; p.147 © Dmitri Ma/ Shutterstock.com; p.148 © Singleline/ Shutterstock.com; pp.150–151 photo by Free to Use Sounds on Unsplash; p.153 © Microgen/Shutterstock.com; pp.154–155 © Scott Anderson IMAGERY/Shutterstock.com; p.156 © Maritxu/Shutterstock.com